GREEK VASES AT YALE

Susan Matheson Burke

Jerome J. Pollitt

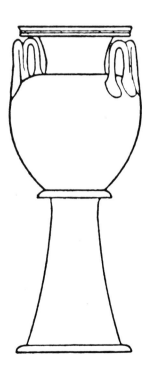

YALE UNIVERSITY ART GALLERY

This catalogue accompanies an exhibition
at the Yale University Art Gallery
between November 19, 1975, and January 18, 1976

Copyright © 1975 by the Yale University Art Gallery
All rights reserved
Library of Congress Catalogue Card Number: 75–24840
Produced under the supervision of Yale University Printing Service
Designed by Klaus Gemming, New Haven, Connecticut
Composed by P&M Typesetting, Waterbury, Connecticut
Printed by The Meriden Gravure Company, Meriden, Connecticut

GREEK VASES AT YALE

CONTRIBUTORS:

Miroslava M. Beneš	MMB
Elizabeth Black	EB
Jeffrey Blanchard	JB
Caroline Bruzelius	CB
Susan Matheson Burke	SMB
Jeffrey Hurwit	JH
Christine Kondoleon	CK
Jeff Kowalski	JK
Carol Ockman	CO
William T. Oedel	WTO
Richard Saunders	RS
Elizabeth Sears	ES
Laura Jean Siegel	LJS
Mary Ellen Carr Soles	MECS
Dicey Taylor	DT

Contents

47

Preface

FOR over half a century Yale University has owned an extensive collection of ancient Greek and Etruscan vases, first assembled by Dr. Paul Arndt of Munich, and acquired for the university in 1913 by Rebecca Darlington Stoddard. The collection is of special interest to students of ancient history, archaeology, and history of art since some 675 vases representing all the known types and ranging over nearly 1500 years of Greek history are included. Because the vases were originally created as utilitarian objects and were also decorated by fine painters, they can be viewed today both as telling documents of Greek life and thought and as products of a highly cultivated aesthetic, all the more valuable since virtually no Greek wall paintings of the earlier periods have survived to the present day. Regrettably, lack of permanent gallery space made it difficult in recent years to show the Stoddard Collection and only a few vases were seen in our Gallery at any given time. We hope the present special exhibition will compensate to some degree for the many years this fine collection has been unavailable to the public.

In addition to the Stoddard vases, nine examples were generously lent to this exhibition by Walter Bareiss, '40S, one of the most knowledgable and tasteful collectors of Greek vases in America. The Bareiss vases significantly augment those in the Stoddard Collection. For instance there is among the Stoddard vases a red-figure amphora from the middle period of the so-called Berlin painter (cat. no. 46), one of the most important vase painters of the period 490–470 B.C. Mr. Bareiss has lent both an early and late work by the same painter (cat. nos. 45 and 47), permitting the study of this artist's stylistic development.

The exhibition was conceived jointly by Professor Jerome J. Pollitt of the Classics and History of Art Departments—and by Mrs. Susan Burke, who is curatorially responsible for the Art Gallery collections of ancient art. Mr. Pollitt and Mrs. Burke selected the seventy-five items in this show and prepared the catalogue in conjunction with students in a graduate seminar offered jointly by the Classics and History of Art Departments in the fall of

1974. An exhibition such as this which utilizes the museum's own resources and involves a collaboration of faculty, curatorial staff, and advanced students provides great satisfaction since it indicates that the museum holdings are directly involved in the teaching and learning process. The Art Gallery is extremely grateful to Mr. Pollitt for the time and effort he devoted to this project, as well as for his enlightening essay on the history and cultural background of vase painting. We are equally indebted to Mrs. Burke. Not only did she contribute to the catalogue and handle all the complex preliminary arrangements for the exhibition, but also devoted the past two years to personally cleaning and restoring a substantial number of the Stoddard vases as part of a long-term conservation project assisted by a grant from the Howard Bayne Fund.

The publication of this catalogue was subsidized in large part by generous contributions from H. J. Heinz, II, '31, chairman of the Art Gallery Governing Board, and Lauder Greenway, '25, a former trustee of the Art Gallery Associates. Their financial and moral support made this exhibition possible.

ALAN SHESTACK, DIRECTOR

Acknowledgements

THIS exhibition and catalogue owe their existence to graduate students in the Departments of Classics, History of Art, and Mediaeval Studies who participated in a seminar in the fall of 1974. Four advanced graduate students contributed their free time to write entries: Caroline Bruzelius (History of Art), Jeffrey Hurwit, Laura Jean Siegel, and Mary Ellen Carr Soles (Classics). In addition, we are grateful to John W. Hayes of the Royal Ontario Museum, whose research notes containing valuable information concerning the date and identification of the vases in the Yale collection, made while a visiting member of the Classics Department in 1967, were graciously made available for reference.

The organizers and authors are especially indebted to Mr. and Mrs. Walter Bareiss and members of their family, both for the loan of vases to supplement and complement the exhibition and for their unfailing hospitality during many visits. A special note of thanks is due Alan Shestack, Director of the Art Gallery, for his continuing support and encouragement.

We are also grateful for help with many specific aspects of the exhibition and catalogue. Robert D. Orr, Jr. designed the installation, which was realized by Robert Soule, Superintendent, and his staff. Joseph Szasfai photographed the vases. For organization, Estelle Miehle, Administrative Assistant, and Fernande Ross, Registrar, deserve special recognition. Our thanks also go to Klaus Gemming, who designed the catalogue, and to Greer Allen and Howard Gralla of the Yale University Printing Service and John Peckham of the Meriden Gravure Company, who supervised the printing.

Many friends and colleagues gave assistance in many ways, and special thinks are due Charles H. Ainsworth, Jr., Marilyn Beckhorn, James D. Burke, Denise D'Avella, Janalyn Gibb, Virginia Greene, Professor Donald Kagan, Elizabeth Kaiser, Patricia Kane, Carla Lucas, Louise Teitz, Paul Tucker, Martha Wolff, and Daniel Arnheim.

Background research by Susan M. Burke on comparative material in European collections was funded in part by a Museum Professional Grant by the Smithsonian Institution, under the provision of the National Museum Act (Public Law 91–629) as amended, and the National Endowment for the Arts.

SUSAN MATHESON BURKE
JEROME J. POLLITT

THE CULTURAL AND HISTORICAL BACKGROUND OF GREEK VASE PAINTING

THE EARLIEST POTTERY in the present exhibition dates from the final phase of the Greek Bronze Age, known technically as Late Helladic III (ca. 1400–1125 B.C.) but generally referred to as "Mycenaean." The century preceding this period had seen a catastrophic decline in the older and artistically more brilliant civilization of Minoan Crete, and during the first sub-phase of this long era (LH IIIA, ca. 1400–1300 B.C.) Mycenaean Greece, now free of Minoan competition, began to emerge as a commercial and military power in the Mediterranean. Whether this Minoan decline and Mycenaean emergence were set in motion by a series of natural disasters, or by a Mycenaean attack on Crete, or by both is a disputed question. It is virtually certain, however, that in the wake of the Minoan collapse contingents of Mycenaeans settled in Crete and gradually absorbed elements of the Minoan artistic and cultural legacy.

In the second sub-phase of this period (LH IIIB, ca. 1300–1200 B.C.) the cities of Mycenaean Greece appear to have attained the peak of their power and prosperity, as their massive fortified citadels, like those at Tiryns and Mycenae, and their elegant palaces, like that at Pylos, testify. Since it seems likely that the royal families of this phase provided the historical prototypes for the legendary heroes and heroines of later Greek epic and drama, it is difficult not to surround the period with a poetic aura; yet from a pragmatic archaeological perspective, its principal historical developments seem to have been commercial expansion and the creation of a meticulously organized, bureaucratic economic system centered in the palaces. Mycenaean pottery of this time, for example, particularly the omi-

present and characteristic stirrup-jar (cat. no. 5), was exported both eastward to Asia Minor, Cyprus, and the Levant and westward to southern Italy and Sicily; and the Linear B tablets found in several Mycenaean palaces give us a picture of an economy in which the products of most industries and occupations, presumably including pottery, were carefully controlled and inventoried by a hierarchy of state officials.

The Mycenaean vases in the present exhibition (cat. nos. 1–6) reflect this historical background in several ways. Their shapes and to an extent their decoration are derived from the Minoan tradition; at the same time their uniformity of fabric and color and their repetitive, schematic decoration all seem to be symptoms of supervised mass production. The bridge-spouted bowl (cat. no. 4) is perhaps the best example of these qualities. Its shape can be traced back through a variety of intermediaries to the Middle Minoan period (ca. 2000–1700 B.C.), and its decorative motifs are shorthand, formulaic versions of naturalistic designs—a sea anemone, a papyrus plant, and a flower—that had once been rendered with loving detail in Minoan art.

Around 1200 B.C. the Mycenaean world began to undergo a series of shocks which ushered in a period of slow decline and ultimate dissolution (LH IIIC, ca. 1200–1125 B.C.). Pylos was destroyed at the very beginning of this period, and the surviving Mycenaean citadels were bolstered by additional fortifications which suggest that they were, for a time at least, under siege. Under siege by whom is a vexed question. By other Mycenaeans? By less sophisticated Greeks from the periphery of the Mycenaean area (e.g. the Dorians of Greek legend)? By the "Sea Peoples" who attacked Egypt during this period? Each of these suggested answers raises difficulties, and hence climatic changes, natural disasters, and pestilence have been invoked to augment the effects of war. Whatever the cause of the decline, by ca. 1125 B.C. many of the old centers of Mycenaean civilization were destroyed and abandoned, there seems to have been a marked decline in population, the population which did survive was pressing or being pressed into new areas, traditional foreign contacts were broken, and new cultural patterns—burial customs, for example—were taking shape.

The pottery produced during this period, along with other archaeological evidence, suggests that in spite of the overall decline an element of cultural continuity remained strong and there were even intervals of revival and invention. In addition to a vigorous if ungainly pictorial style and a style based on closely packed patterns of curving lines that seemed to preserve some of the old Minoan elegance, there was a substantial amount of routinely decorated pottery clearly descended from the standard products of LH IIIB. The stirrup jar in the present exhibition (cat. no. 5) is a good example of this last variety. Its globular shape and perfunctory decoration mark it as a late product, but otherwise it reveals no drastic break with earlier tradition. The fact that this vessel is said to have come from near Patras may have historical significance. There is evidence that when Mycenae came under attack refugees from the Argolid sought shelter in Achaia, a more remote and backward, but at this time apparently safer, region of the Peloponnesus. Our stirrup jar, in the tradition of finer and earlier Mycenaean pottery but seemingly made for less demanding clients, may be the work of one of these refugees.

Still another style of pottery produced during the LH IIIC period, the "Granary Style" (named after the building at Mycenae where substantial amounts of it were found), is of interest because it points not to the fading past but to an obscure yet fruitful future. The Granary Style is characterized by simple, casually painted banded decoration, sometimes augmented with sketchy, widely-spaced linear ornaments. The clay used for vessels decorated in this style tends to be coarse and the paint is often thin and dull. In the present exhibition the three-handled jar from Rhodes (cat. no. 6), while not one of the most typical shapes, provides a good example of the general quality of the Granary Style. It was pottery of this type that survived the final collapse of Mycenae and served as the point of departure which led ultimately to the Protogeometric and Geometric styles.

The two centuries that follow the fall of Mycenaean civilization are the most obscure in Greek history and are customarily referred to as the "Dark Age." Since there are no written records from this period, its history, to the extent that one can use the term, has to be deduced from disparate and complex archaeological evidence. Most of the remains of the Submycenaean (ca. 1125–1050 B.C.) and Protogeometric (ca. 1050–900 B.C.) periods come from cemeteries. These are often found above and within areas earlier inhabited and subsequently abandoned by Mycenaeans and are characterized by cist or earth-cut graves with single burials that contrast markedly with the chamber tombs of the Mycenaean period. Among the vases found in these graves there are palsied examples of the stirrup jar which represent the last flicker of the principal Mycenaean tradition, but more typical are the cups, pitchers, and amphorae which are descended from the LH IIIC Granary Style. The late Submycenaean amphora in the present exhibition (cat. no. 7) is an excellent example of this class. Cremation made its first significant appearance in Greece at this time, and amphorae like this one often served as ash urns. They also sometimes contained, or were found with, new types of long pins that seem to have been connected with a new type of dress. A few of these pins are of iron, which also makes its first significant appearance. Taken together these new customs, artifacts, and materials suggest a period of thoroughgoing cultural change in which new elements entered the population of Greece and merged with other elements in a complex pattern of migration and resettlement.

Although the history of the succeeding Protogeometric period is no less obscure than that of the Submycenaean, one gets the feeling by looking at its pottery that important psychological changes have taken place, that there has been a reintegration of the population of Greece, and that a new cultural character has begun to take shape. To reach such conclusions one must use the abstract decoration of Protogeometric pottery as if it were a kind of cultural Rorschach test that enables one to see into the mentality of its creators. It is instructive to compare our late Submycenaean amphora (cat. no. 7) with the Protogeometric amphora also on display in the present exhibition (cat. no. 8). The Submycenaean vase carries on, as noted, the rather casual decorative tradition of the Granary Style. A freehand, irregular design made up of two curving lines decorates its shoulder, and three sets of bands are applied seemingly at random to the body of the vase. The Protogeometric vase painter, by contrast, has arranged his decoration in such a way that it both analyzes and emphasizes the structure of the vessel. Two sets of bands are placed at points on the body of the vessel where its curvature becomes most acute, thus separating the main expanse of the vessel from its terminations. To emphasize the curvature of the shoulders and of the handles that join the body to the neck, the painter has applied not a freehand design but rather sets of precise concentric circles drawn with a multiple brush compass. This urge for geometric exactitude, for a harmonious interrelation of parts, and for an understanding of how things are put together is something new in Greek art and can be understood as the first glimmer of the artistic predilections and philosophical disposition that will characterize the subsequent development of Greek culture. One feels that Hellenic as opposed to Helladic art has begun.

The Protogeometric Style seems to have originated in Athens, and it is in Athens that the subsequent Geometric Style (ca. 900–700 B.C.) reaches its most impressive level of development. In this style the incipient taste for geometric ornament of the Protogeometric period grows into a complex system of banded decoration that draws upon a large repertoire of Geometric motifs—meanders, lozenges, triangles, and the like. Human and animal figures gradually become common in the style, but they are always rigorously geometricized and subordinated to the decorative rules of the system. The masterpieces of the mature Geometric Style are the great Dipylon vases which stood as grave markers in the cemeteries of Athens, but its essential character can readily be seen and appreciated in pieces like the pomegranate vase (cat. no. 9) and the standed bowl (cat. no. 11) in the present exhibition.

During the period when the Geometric Style was in vogue certain basic historical developments are assumed to have taken place in Greece. It seems likely that the city-states which were to dominate later Greek history began to assume their distinctive characters, that there was a growth of population which eventually stimulated the beginning of overseas colonization, and that a concept of cultural unity, symbolized by the founding of the Olympic Games, came to be appreciated in all the major areas of the country. The distribution and variety of Geometric pottery can be taken as archaeological evidence in support of these assumptions: the style was widespread in Greece yet in each area it preserved an individual character (compare, for example, the Attic vases in the present exhibition with the example from Boeotia, cat. no. 23); and toward the end of the period it began to appear in Italy.

What many modern students of Antiquity would consider the most memorable development of the era, however, was the creation of the Homeric epics, which seem to have been composed somewhere between 750 and 700 B.C. While the analogy should not be pressed too far, it is possible to see a certain similarity between the psychological processes by which the epics and the masterpieces of the Geometric style were created. The epic poet drew upon a venerable tradition of oral poetry, developed perhaps over several centuries, in which stock epithets, phrases, and scenes had been gradually brought to perfection. Using these preformed building blocks, the poet of the *Iliad* shaped a carefully designed narrative in which a focal human drama was set into a matrix of traditional material. In the same way a painter of the mature Geometric Style assembled decorative motifs that had been developed and handed down over several generations to create traditional settings into which he could insert narrative scenes of battles, hunts, and funerals which gave his entire composition a particular focus. Carrying the analogy a step further we may also note that in both the poems and the vases the artist remains relatively anonymous, with his individuality and tastes largely merged in the conventions of the style.

So often in the history of Greek art and society, a period of relative stability, in which certain forms and ideas are patiently perfected, is followed by a period of disintegration, experiment, and change which eventually leads to a new period of order and synthesis. The seventh century B.C. in an example of the latter. The movement toward overseas colonization that began toward the end of the eighth century B.C. and the increased foreign trade that went with it brought the Greeks once again into contact with the cultural resources of the ancient Near East. Under the impact of new ideas and institutions arising from this contact—myths, literary models, alphabetic writing, artistic motifs, sculptural techniques—the insularity of Geometric Greece slowly crumbled, and an age of wide-ranging innovation ensued. Of the many regional styles of Greek pottery that developed during this "Orientaliz-

ing" period (ca. 700–625 B.C.) two are of particular importance: Protoattic and Protocorinthian. Painters in both schools adopted a variety of curvilinear designs, floral motifs, and animal friezes that were of eastern origin, and both began to depict specific Greek myths and legends. Their techniques and tastes, however, differed markedly. The Attic painters used an outline technique and preferred to work on a relatively large surface; the painters of developed Protocorinthian worked mostly on a miniature scale and painted their figures in black silhouette to which details were later added by incision. The work of Attica was characterized by ambitious, if at times awkward, narration; that of Corinth by formal precision. Although a hint of the beginning of the Protoattic style may be seen in the S-curve decorations on a high-standed bowl in the present exhibition (cat. no. 13), the full development of the style can only be illustrated by reference to works like the Nessos amphora in the Metropolitan Museum in New York (see R.M. Cook, *Greek Painted Pottery* [London 1973] pl. 16). Several typical examples of the Protocorinthian Style, however, are represented here (cat. nos. 14–16). On their background and character see *infra* p. 11–12

Toward the end of the seventh century B.C. a fusion of these two styles, combining the precise incised silhouette of Protocorinthian with the monumentality of Protoattic, takes place in Athens, and the result is one of the great genres of Greek art, Attic black-figure. In the early stage of the black-figure tradition there is a very strong Corinthian stylistic element (see cat. nos. 27–29), and it is difficult to avoid the conclusion that a number of Corinthian potters and vase-painters migrated to Athens around 600 B.C. While no ancient source mentions such a movement, the political conditions of Athens and Corinth at this time lend credibility to the idea. During the second half of the seventh century B.C. Corinth was ruled by the tyrant Cypselus (traditionally

652–625 B.C.) and subsequently by his son Periander (traditionally 625–585 B.C.). Cypselus, who overthrew the oligarchic Bacchiad clan that had ruled Corinth for about a century, was admired by the Corinthian populace and won fame as one of the first important patrons of the arts in Greece. It is probably not a coincidence that the masterpieces of Protocorinthian painting date from his reign. Periander, by contrast, could maintain power only through a repressive regime that ruthlessly eliminated citizens who seemed to be accumulating too much power. One aspect of this policy was the setting of strict limits on the amount of wealth that could be accumulated. While Periander ruled at Corinth a series of constitutional and legal reforms which substantially improved the lot of the lower classes were being instituted in Athens under the guidance of the philosopher, poet, and politician Solon. These changes resulted in a reinvigorated economic system in which craftsmen with useful skills from other Greek cities were encouraged to settle in Athens and became eligible for Athenian citizenship. In the face of repression and economic restraints at home, it is not unlikely that some Corinthian potters were strongly attracted by the opportunity to work in a newly liberalized Athens where tradesmen could freely profit from their skills.

Once the Attic black-figure style was developed, it quickly became the dominant form of pottery in the Greek world. Other regional schools using a roughly similar technique but lacking its finesse run parallel to it for a time (see cat. nos. 24–26), but most of them fade away by the end of the sixth century B.C. From the Archaic period onward the history of Greek vase painting thus becomes largely the history of Athenian vase painting.

During most of the heyday of the black-figure style Athens was controlled by the tyrant Peisistratus (560–527 B.C., with interruptions) and his sons (527–510 B.C.), and the cultural atmosphere which these resourceful and in many ways enlightened leaders brought to the city had its effect on the artists of the time. Peisistratus was the greatest literary patron of early Greece. He retained scholarly poets to collate a definitive text of the Homeric epics; a contest to honor the rhapsodes who recited the epics was incorporated into the Panathenaic festival; and, toward the end of his reign, tragedy was recognized as a distinctive genre of Attic choral poetry, and dramatic contests were introduced as part of a civic festival. Given the taste which this background implies, it is not surprising that much of the subject matter of the best black-figure vase painting of the time was inspired by the myths and sagas of heroic, and particularly epic, poetry and that in the hands of its greatest practitioners, like Exekias, the style could express a solemn, tragic intensity. Heroic combats, as one might expect, were particularly common themes, and the battles on the splendid eye-kylix in the present exhibition (cat. no. 34) provide typical examples of this iconographic tradition.

The technical innovation which led to the creation of the Attic red-figure style around 530 B.C.—i.e. the reserving of what had previously been painted and the painting of what had previously been reserved—may have occurred at first simply as a casual decorative experiment. The earliest group of painters in this style often painted "bilinguals," vases that were done partly in red-figure and partly in the black-figure style, like the kylix by the painter Oltos in the present exhibition (cat. no. 41). In these and other early red-figure works the most typical stylistic features—neat profiles and painstakingly applied ornamental detail—are still closely tied to the conventions of black-figure. Within fifteen or twenty years from the invention of red-figure, however, a group of very gifted painters began to see previously untapped expressive possibilities in the new style and inaugurated an exciting era of experimentation in both style and subject matter.

The red-figure style has a way of forcing the eye to concentrate on the internal structure of individual figures rather than on an overall pattern formed by a group of figures, as in black-figure. The great early experimenters in red-figure, e.g. Euphronios and Euthymides, undoubtedly realized this. They may also have felt that with the perfection of the highly patternized, incised silhouette in the work of Exekias, black-figure had reached the limits of its possible development, and there was little left for them to do. In any case, they now turned with enthusiasm to the delineation of the individual man in three essential aspects: how he is put together; how he appears to others; and how he functions in his natural environment. The musculature of the body is now studied closely. Foreshortened views of the body as it twists and moves in space now become objects of fascination. Scenes from the world of the ordinary citizen—athletes exercising in the gymnasium, youths and courtesans enjoying drinking parties and suffering their after-effects, women washing clothing—become as common as scenes from the world of epic heroes. These features are well represented in the present exhibition by the symposion scene on a kylix associated with the style of the Gales Painter (cat. no. 42) and by the jumper on a kylix by the Chaire Painter (cat. no. 48).

While historical conditions by themselves cannot account for the rise of artistic styles, it is once again possible to point to political and social changes which may have abetted the red-figure style in taking the course that it did. In 514 B.C. one of the sons of Peisistratus was assassinated, and the other was overthrown in 510. In the wake of the fall of the Peisistratidai democratic government was restored to Athens, and a new constitution was drawn up by the statesman Cleisthenes. This constitution contained far-reaching reforms that were designed to involve the average citizen much more actively in the day-to-day life of the city.

While it is an oversimplification to see this change as one from cruel autocracy to pure democracy (the Peisistratid rule was in many ways humane, and the Cleisthenean democracy was in many ways aristocratic), there can be little doubt that it did bring with it a more democratic atmosphere, one in which the cultured, refined, literate preoccupations of the Peisistratid court yielded to a concern with the experience of the ordinary citizen. And it is this shift, as already observed, that is mirrored in the change from mature black-figure to early red-figure.

The naturalistic, humanistic trend in early red-figure reaches its culmination in the work of the Berlin Painter (cat. nos. 45–47) around 490 B.C. One feels here that the aggressive experimentation of the previous two decades had been digested and that the painter wanted the perfection of his individual figures to shine forth in a simple radiance unalloyed by the surrounding complexity of traditional ornament. The sobriety of the Yale amphora by this painter (cat. no. 46) seems to hint at a new tone, one that was to pervade Greek art after the next great drama of Greek history, the Persian Wars, was played out.

The invasion of Greece by the army of an enormous Oriental empire, beginning with the battle of Marathon in 490 B.C. and culminating with the battle of Plataea in 479, left a lasting impression on the Greek cultural character. The trauma of near defeat and the self-confidence born of ultimate triumph brought with them a contemplative atmosphere in which the mutability of the human condition and the moral consequences of action became subjects of intense scrutiny. Consciousness, states of mind, and the anguish of doubt enter into the subject matter of the greatest works of Greek art and literature such as the sculptures from the temple of Zeus at Olympia and the dramas of Aeschylus. Literary sources suggest that the great painters of the time, like Polygnotos of Thasos, were more interested in suggesting moods than in depicting action and strove to convey the *ethos*, the essential character, of their figures. A good example of this trend can be seen in the dignified figures of Theseus and Poseidon by the Painter of the Yale Oinochoe (cat. no. 54). The story of Theseus's patrimony as well as the possible contemporary political overtones of the two figures are not explicitly shown. Rather the viewer is invited to use his own powers of thought to grasp these themes and their significance in the calm and meditative figures put before him.

From about the middle of the fifth century B.C. onward there were developments in Greek mural and panel painting, e.g. shading and the rendering of spatial perspective, which clashed with the technical limitations and aesthetic demands of vase painting. As these changes took place vase painting declined to the status of a minor art in which elegance of decoration superseded the tight integration of form and content of previous periods. The decline was gradual, however, and there continued to be gifted painters whose work embodies the essential character of the art of their era. The Achilles Painter, for example, captured the aloof, imperturbable Olympianism of the Pheidian style in sculpture, the style which served as an outward expression of the cultured self-confidence and optimism of Periclean Athens. In the present exhibition the distinctive mixture of action and aloofness in the amphora by the Painter of the Boston Phiale (cat. no. 57) belongs to the same tradition.

During the last third of the fifth century B.C. Greek sculpture was dominated by stylistic mannerisms that had been developed in the late stages of the Parthenon school. The most obvious of these is a fascination with complex, calligraphic patterns of swirling drapery, most often used to enhance graceful female figures like those of the Nike Parapet on the Acropolis in Athens. The vase painters of this period adopted this style with alacrity and even seem to have enhanced the feminine, cosmetic aspects of it. Scenes of heroic struggle were increasingly forsaken in favor of scenes in which elegantly dressed groups of women, or lovers, or both are posed as if in a fashion show. The outstanding practitioner of this style was the Meidias Painter, and a squat lekythos in the present exhibition (cat. no. 61), by a gifted follower of this painter if not by the master himself, provides an excellent example of the character of his work.

It may seem strange that this seemingly untroubled, ornate style should be the one that dominates Athenian vase-painting during the long and wasting Peloponnesian War (431–404 B.C.). No hint of the anguish expressed in Euripides' *Trojan Women* or *Bacchae* is allowed to disturb the boudoir-like seclusion of the Meidian world, where even scenes of violence are transmuted into something painless and genteel. It may be that the Meidian style appealed to and was sustained by some sort of escapist instinct and that the elegant fantasy world of these pots provided their owners with a moment of psychological respite in a period of strife and increasing hardship.

During the years when Athens was locked into its bitter struggle with the Peloponnesians, the Athenian potters lost contact with their once lucrative market in Italy and Sicily, and the Greek settlers in these areas began to make their own red-figure pottery (see cat. nos. 66–68). In its early stages South Italian red-figure has a crispness rivalling that of its Athenian models (e.g. the bell krater by the Dolon Painter, cat. no. 66), but as the fourth century B.C. progresses they take on a floridity and a looseness of technique that is all their own (see cat. nos. 67 and 68). As Athens recovered from the effects of the Peloponnesian War during the fourth century, potters continued to work in the red-figure style and eventually even found a new overseas market for their wares among the cities on the coast of the Black Sea. In a general way Attic red-figure in the fourth century carries on the elegant style of the late fifth century with emphasis at first on its ornamental pageantry and later, as the "Kerch Style" (see p. 79–82) developed, on its feminine elegance. The figures on Kerch Style vases (e.g. cat. no. 65) have at their best a statuesque refinement that connects them with the sculpture of Praxiteles and perhaps also with the *charis*, "grace," that ancient writers ascribed to the famous painter Apelles.

These allusions to the major arts point up the predicament in which the late red-figure painters found themselves, a predicament that perhaps ultimately brought about the extinction of the style. Literary sources make clear that the great painters who worked in monumental media during this period made increasingly sophisticated and subtle use of color and of those techniques for rendering light and space that the painters of the fifth century had introduced. As public taste in painting became attuned to these innovations red-figure may have begun to look primitive. At the same time its emphasis on figural narrative and its limited chromatic range prevented it from attaining the pure ornamentality that could be achieved in vessels made of materials like metal and glass. Other types of pottery, like Gnathian ware (cat. nos. 67–72) and Megarian bowls (cat. nos. 73–75) could do this, and it was these styles that carried the Greek ceramic tradition into the Hellenistic period when Attic red-figure and its South Italian offshoot died out after ca. 320 B.C.

JEROME J. POLLITT

THE TECHNIQUES OF GREEK POTTERY

TECHNIQUE is often a determining factor in the development of style. This was particularly true in Greek vase painting, where the technical change from black-figure to red-figure resulted in a new concern for depth and movement that transformed the style of vase paintings. The new red-figure technique permitted a more fluid line. The black-figure silhouette which emphasized joints and profiles was succeeded by red-figure line drawing which created fuller, rounder forms that could twist and turn in space. For the generation or two when both techniques coexisted, black-figure paintings retained their flat decorative character while red-figure artists explored the movement of the body in space. The limits imposed on the black-figure artist during this time were largely those of technique.

In order that the viewer might better understand the technical limitations on the Greek vase painter and more fully appreciate his success in working within this medium, it seems appropriate to describe briefly the techniques used, particularly for black-figure and red-figure vases. Other types of pottery manufacture, for example the mold-made Megarian bowls, have been described in the relevant entries.

All of the pottery in this exhibition was made on a potter's wheel. Large vessels were generally made in sections, the body in two or more parts and the neck added separately. Feet, handles and mouth were made separately and added on to the completed body. The construction of the vessel is frequently visible in its profile. A sharp edge or acute angle, as on the shoulder of a lekythos or the base of the neck of a stamnos, for example, indicates the joining of two parts. A continuous curve, such as that merging the neck to the body of a pelike, suggests a single, unified action. The primary exception to this visual rule is at the point of maximum diameter of the body of large vessels. Joins here are frequent, but the exterior surface is carefully smoothed by the potter to give the appearance of a continuous curve, of a vessel made in one piece.

Local clay was used in most cases. Of course this varied in color and composition from place to place and is often used as a distinguishing feature in localizing vessels. Attic clay is pinker than Corinthian, for example, due to a higher content of ferric oxide (Fe_2O_3). It is this same ferric oxide that produces the characteristic colors of Attic black and red-figure pottery.

To follow one vessel through the entire process of its manufacture, one must start with the digging of the clay. A black-figure vessel will be used in this summary for convenience. Most of the procedure is identical for both black and red-figure vases; differences will be noted as they occur. Once dug, the clay was left to weather. Next the potter levigated it, that is, mixed it with water and left it to stand until the coarser particles in the clay had settled to the bottom, leaving the finer particles still in suspension. The suspension of finer particles was run off and set aside, to be used later in the decoration of the vase. The coarser clay was left to dry until stiff enough for kneading and working. The vessel was then formed on the potter's wheel and left to dry until leather hard. The potter and painter of a vessel were not always the same person; at this point the painter would begin.

The first stage of decoration was to coat the entire vessel with a thin wash of ochre. This served to intensify the red color of the clay. The painter then burnished the vessel, smoothing and consolidating the surface. Possibly before but more probably after this step, the red-figure artist often sketched his composition with some hard instrument that pressed into the clay. These sketches can best be seen in a raking light. The fact that they do not always coincide with the finished drawing shows that the artist made changes while he worked. Sketches of this kind occur only rarely on black-figure vessels, and it seems that if the black-figure artist made sketches at all they were of some perishable material such as charcoal that disappeared or was covered by subsequent decoration.

Next the solid areas of black glaze and the decoration were painted on with a fine brush, using the suspension of finer clay particles saved from the earlier levigation process as the black glaze matter. Only the black silhouettes of the figures were applied in this step. Areas that were to remain red in the finished vessel were left unpainted (reserved). Added red and white were applied next, and finally the details were incised with a sharp instrument. After a drying period, the vase was ready for firing.

The procedure for decorating a red-figure vessel differed in a critical way. Instead of painting a black silhouette for the figures, they were outlined with a broad band of black glaze (contour line), and the figure itself was left in reserve (unpainted). Interior lines were drawn with a thick black glaze (relief line), which was sometimes used to reinforce the contour of the figure as well. Added red occurs fairly often in red-figure, but added white is rare until the late fifth century, even for the hair of old men. Anatomical details, a special concern of early red-figure artists, were normally added in dilute black glaze which appeared as a thin reddish brown color on the finished vessel. Other elements of the composition, architecture, furniture, plants, and decorative motifs were treated in the same way. The background on red-figure vessels is a solid black, exactly the reverse of the black-figure technique. The reserved figures immediately possessed a roundness and solidity lacking in the flat silhouettes of black-figure. With only the minimal suggestion of one curving line a spine could twist and turn, and foreshortening was easily suggested.

At this stage the final black and red colors

on the vessel varied only in tone. The sharp contrast between shiny black and the reserved red of the clay appeared only after firing.

The vases were fired in a kiln, although the details of its design are uncertain. There were three stages in the firing of an Attic vessel. The first was an oxidizing phase. Oxygen was present and the kiln temperature was probably about 800°C. Under these conditions the ferric oxide in the clay was unaffected and the vessel retained its red color. In the second, or reducing phase, the atmosphere was deprived of oxygen, and the temperature was raised to about 950°C. During this stage the vessel became black because oxygen from the ferric oxide was absorbed into the atmosphere, leaving behind one of the black iron oxides (FeO or Fe_3O_4). Greek vases that have been in fires at some time in their subsequent history revert to this grey-black stage.

The third stage was oxidizing again, with the temperature lowered to about 900°C, and under these conditions the entire vessel would have turned red as the black iron oxides absorbed oxygen were it not for one other feature. At temperatures of between 825° and 950°C a partial vitrification of the Greek clay occurs in which the particles of iron oxide become enclosed in quartz crystals which are also present in the clay. This partial vitrification or sintering prevents the clay from reabsorbing oxygen and again becoming red. Sintering only occurs in the more refined clay, thus it occurs only in the black glaze matter, while the re-mainder of the vessel, being made of coarser clay, can be reoxidized. The parts of the vessel coated with black glaze thus remained black in the third stage of firing, while the reserved areas reoxidized and became red. If the black glaze were applied too thinly there would not have been sufficient sintering to prevent reoxidation, and the entire vessel would misfire red. Sintering, together with burnishing before the vessel is decorated and the possible addition of a peptizing agent such as potash, seem to be responsible for the sheen that is characteristic of Attic vases.

Since no written record describing these processes survives, our understanding of the ancient techniques must be to some extent empirical. Remains of several kilns have helped in determining their design, as have a few terra cotta plaques showing potters at work. Test pieces and unfinished vessels have added to our understanding of the sequence of procedures. Representations of potters and painters at work on the vases themselves have shown us something of the appearance and hierarchy of the pottery workshops and have even demonstrated that, in one case at least, women were active members of these workshops. The rest of our knowledge is based on successful modern attempts to recreate the process and on continuing scientific analysis of the materials used by the Greeks.

SUSAN MATHESON BURKE

Amphora   Hydria   Lebes Gamikos   Loutrophoros

Skyphos   Aryballos   Alabastron   Pyxis

Kantharos   Kylix   Lekythos   Squat Lekythos   Oinochoe

Column Krater   Bell Krater   Pelike   Stamnos

Shapes of Greek Vases

ALABASTRON: elongated perfume vessel with narrow neck; name derived from the original material of the vessel.

AMPHORA: two-handled jar, with handles reaching from body to neck or mouth. Storage jar for both solids and liquids, and as a measure.

ARYBALLOS: narrow necked oil bottle, commonly used by athletes.

HYDRIA: three-handled water jar, side handles for lifting, vertical handle for pouring. Use determined from vase paintings.

KANTHAROS: two-handled cup with deep bowl and high foot.

KRATER: wide mouthed, broad bodied vessel, used for mixing wine and water. Use based on literary evidence. *Column Krater:* named for columnar shape of handles. *Bell Krater:* krater with bell shaped body.

KYLIX: two-handled drinking cup with shallow bowl and high foot.

LEBES GAMIKOS: "Marriage Bowl." A bowl with foot and vertical handles from the shoulder, an adaptation of the lebes (round bottomed bowl or *dinos*) with separate stand. Shown as a wedding gift in vase paintings.

LEKYTHOS: jug with one handle, narrow neck and deep mouth, used for oil and unguents, as an athlete's oil bottle or a woman's toilet bottle, and as a tomb offering. *Squat Lekythos:* variant with squat body, broad base and no distinct shoulder.

LOUTROPHOROS: tall vessel with slender body, tall thin neck and flaring mouth. Used for carrying water, especially for the nuptial bath, and as a tomb offering for unmarried persons.

OINOCHOE: jug, used for ladling and pouring wine. *Chous:* variant with bulbous body and trefoil mouth. *Olpe:* conventional name for oinochoe with slender shape and continuous curve.

PELIKE: variety of amphora, neck and body forming continuous curve, widest portion of body near base.

PYXIS: round toilet or medicine box, with lid.

SKYPHOS or KOTYLE: deep drinking cup with low foot and two handles. *Kotyle:* a generic Greek word for cup rather than a specific shape name, used conventionally.

STAMNOS: storage vessel, usually with lid, which is often lost. Ancient evidence for relation of name to shape uncertain, name retained for convenience.

Abbreviations

AJA: American Journal of Archaeology

AthMitt: Mitteilungen des Deutschen Archäologischen Instituts: Römische Abteilung.

Baur, *Stoddard Catalogue:* Paul V. C. Baur, *Catalogue of the Rebecca Darlington Stoddard Collection of Greek and Italian Vases in Yale University* (New Haven 1922)

Beazley, *ABV:* J. D. Beazley, *Attic Black-Figure Vase Painters* (Oxford 1956)

Beazley, *ARV²:* J. D. Beazley, *Attic Red-Figure Vase Painters,* second edition (Oxford 1963)

Beazley, *Paralipomena:* J. D. Beazley, *Paralipomena, Additions to Attic Black-Figure Vase Painters and to Attic Red-Figure Vase Painters* (Oxford 1971)

Beazley, *VA:* J. D. Beazley, *Attic Red-figured Vases in American Museums* (Cambridge, Mass. 1918)

von Bothmer, *MMA Exh:* Dietrich von Bothmer and Jacob Bean, *Greek Vases and Modern Drawings from the Collection of Mr. and Mrs. Walter Bareiss,* exhibition checklist, Metropolitan Museum of Art, New York, N. D. (1969)

Brommer, *Vasenlisten:* Frank Brommer, *Vasenlisten zur griechischen Heldensagen* (Marburg 1973)

BSA: Annual of the British School at Athens

Buitron, *NEC:* Diana M. Buitron, *Attic Vase Painting in New England Collections,* exhibition catalogue, Fogg Art Museum, Cambridge, Mass. 1972

CVA: Corpus Vasorum Antiquorum

Furumark, *MPA:* Arne Furumark, *The Mycenaean Pottery: Analysis and Classification* (Stockholm 1972)

Haspels, *ABL:* C. H. E. Haspels, *Attic Black-figured Lekythoi* (Paris 1936)

JdI: Jahrbuch des Deutschen Archäologischen Instituts

JHS: Journal of Hellenic Studies

Richter, *RFV:* G. M. A. Richter, *Attic Red-Figured Vases, a Survey* (New Haven 1946)

RömMitt: Mitteilungen des Deutschen Archäologischen Instituts: Römische Abteilung

Trendall, *LCS:* A. D. Trendall, *The Red-Figured Vases of Lucania, Campania and Sicily* (Oxford 1967)

1, 2, 5

MYCENAEAN POTTERY

Mycenaean pottery was the product of an imperial civilization. Through trade and colonization, a consistent Mycenaean style was spread throughout the Eastern Mediterraean. Mycenaean vases have been found in Crete, Cyprus, Palestine, Turkey (Anatolia) and Egypt.

The uniformity of Mycenaean pottery at any period in its development leads to studies based on classification and typology. Relative chronology is elicited from the evolution of shape and decorative motifs. Absolute chronology depends on external evidence.

Mycenaean potters were quite clearly subject to influences from styles other than their own. The basic stylistic impetus for Mycenaean pottery has long been recognized as Minoan. The piriform jar seen here virtually in miniature frequently served in a much larger version as a storage jar in the places of Crete and the mainland. The shape of our Mycenaean jar echoes its vigorous Minoan prototype. Specific shapes sometimes reflect vessels from civilizations other than the Minoan, probably seen through trade. The squat alabastron (cat. no. 2), a shape borrowed from the baggy Egyptian vessel of the same name is one of these. These two vessels were made towards the beginning of the Mycenaean Empire, ca. 1350 B.C. Although modest, they show quite clearly the energetic profile and elegant curves that characterized the best of Mycenaean Palace Art.

The bridge-spouted bowl (cat. no. 3) and the waisted cup (cat. no. 4) survive from the second phase of the Mycenaean Empire, which ended in destruction around 1200 B.C. Both vessels are from Rhodes, the site of a thriving Mycenaean colony at this time. The papyrus plants that adorn the spouted bowl are conventionalized memories of Minoan motifs, acknowledging the Cretan love of nature but imposing on it a stylized restraint. The shape derives from a Late Minoan I B metal prototype; this particular variation is common on Rhodes (Furumark *MPA 637*). The circles and crosses on the waisted cup are but a remote cousin of the running spiral from which they are decended.

The false-necked or stirrup jar (cat. no. 5) was perhaps the most characteristic Mycenaean shape. Derived again from the Minoan, the shape undergoes an evolution parallel to that of many other vessels. Lively, often exaggerated curves with squat or elegantly piriform profiles give way after the destruction of the palaces to the simpler globular form of this example. The semi-circle within a triangle, usually applied to stirrup jars, best shows the link between Crete and Cyprus in the predestruction period. Here it is seen in a late product of the mainland, found near Patras.

1. Piriform Jar

Mycenaean. Late Helladic III A:2 Ca. 1400–1300 B.C. Yale University Art Gallery 1967.74.2.

Dimensions: H. 14.3 cm.; D. 13 cm.

Description: Buff fabric, with glaze fired reddish brown. Horizontal bands on the body with a "v" pattern (Furumark, *MPA* motif 59) on the shoulder. Three handles.

Condition: Intact.

2. Squat Alabastron

Mycenaean. Late Helladic III A:2. Ca. 1400–1300 B.C. Stoddard Collection. Yale University Art Gallery 1913.42.
Dimensions: H. 5.8 cm.; D. 8.6 cm.

Description: Buff fabric with the glaze fired an uneven reddish brown. Continuous wave pattern (Furumark *MPA* motif 32, type 5) around the lower body. Three handles.

Condition: Unbroken, but a large chip out of the rim and numerous chips out of the body.

Bibliography: Baur, *Stoddard Catalogue* 42, fig. 6.

3. Bridge-spouted Bowl

Mycenaean. Late Helladic III B. Ca. 1300–1200 B.C. Stoddard Collection. Yale University Art Gallery 1913.44.

Dimensions: H. 15.6 cm.; D. 26 cm.

Description: Buff fabric, glaze fired red. Bands on the body, papyrus (Furumark *MPA* motif 11, type 51 etc.) in the handle zone.

Condition: Broken and repaired with plaster restorations, some of which are painted.

Provenance: From Rhodes.

Bibliography: Baur, *Stoddard Catalogue* 42–3, fig. 6; Furumark, *MPA* 637.

3

4

4. Waisted Cup

Mycenaean. Late Helladic III B. Ca. 1300–1200 B.C. *Stoddard Collection. Yale University Art Gallery 1913.45.*

Dimensions: H. 17.4 cm.; D. 16.6 cm.

Description: Pinkish fabric with buff slip, glaze fired red. Two bands of curtailed running spirals (Furumark, *MPA* motif 46, type 25) encircle the body.

Condition: Strain crack in the side wall, chip out of the rim.

Provenance: From Rhodes.

Bibliography: Baur, *Stoddard Catalogue* 43, fig. 6; Furmark, *MPA* 623, no. 226.

5. Stirrup Jar

Mycenaean. Late Helladic III C:1. Ca. 1200–1100 B.C. *Stoddard Collection. Yale University Art Gallery 1913.34.*

Dimensions: H. 11 cm.; D. 10.7 cm.

Description: Buff fabric, glaze fired brownish red. Lower body covered with solid red glaze. Bands encircle the rest of the body below the shoulder zone; the shoulder zone decoration consists of semi-circles on the neck side and semi-circles with triangles on the opposite side (Furumark *MPA* motif 43, type 58).

Condition: Broken and repaired with painted restoration on the lower body. Chips out of the top of the false neck and the side of the body opposite the true neck.

Provenance: Said to have been found near Patras.

Bibliography: Baur, *Stoddard Catalogue* 39–40, fig. 6. For closely related stirrup jars from Cyprus and Crete, see V. R. d'A. Desborough, *The Last Mycenaeans and their Successors* (Oxford 1964) 26–7, pl. 18.

6

6. Three-handled Jar

Mycenaean. Late Helladic III C:1. Ca. 1200–1100 B.C. Stoddard Collection. Yale University Art Gallery 1913.37.

Dimensions: H. 45.9 cm.

Description: Ovoid conical, Furumark, *MPA* type 38. Brownish fabric, glaze fabric mostly dark brown. Three groups of bands encircle the body. On the shoulder, between ribbed handles, disintegrated tricurved arches of LH III C:1 date (Furumark, *MPA* motif 62, near type 33).

Condition: Intact.

Provenance: From Rhodes.

Bibliography: Baur, *Stoddard Catalogue* 41, fig. 7.

S. M. B.

7. Neck-handled Amphora

Submycenaean. Ca. 1075–1050 B.C. Stoddard Collection. Yale University Art Gallery 1913.49.

Submycenaean pottery follows immediately upon the last phase of Mycenaean proper, Late Helladic III C: 1c. Shapes and decorative motifs continue from one to the other, but the Submycenaean vessels are heavier, more globular and static than their predecessors. Profiles become simpler, curves less exaggerated. This restraint increases in Geometric vessels. Decorative motifs, frequently confined to the handle zone, are thoroughly simplified, if not degenerated.

The tombs of the Kerameikos in Athens have yielded some close parallels in shape for our amphora (W. Kraiker and Karl Kübler, *Kerameikos* I [Berlin 1939] pl. 26, grave 56, inv. 422 and grave 75, inv. 519). These are considered by Arne Furumark ("The Mycenaean III C Pottery and its Relation to Cypriote Fabrics," *Opuscula Archaeologica* 3 [1944] 221) to be typically Submycenaean and are dated by C. G. Styrenius to ca. 1075–1050 B.C. (*Submycenaean Studies* [Lund 1967] 63). Both these amphorae were cremation urns, the only two in the Late Submycenaean A levels of the Kerameikos. Inhumation was still the most common burial form during the Late Submycenaean, although cremations increased steadily throughout the period.

The date for Submycenaean pottery cannot be determined from the evidence provided by finds on the Greek mainland. Only by cross references to Cypriote and Palestinian pottery and other evidence outside the mainland can the provisional date spanning the middle twelfth to the middle eleventh century by assigned.

Dimensions: H. 41.3 cm.

Description: Buff fabric with the glaze fired dark brown. Horizontal bands on the body, antithetical curves on the shoulder between and at the base of the handles. A cross on each handle.

Condition: Broken at the base of the neck and handles and repaired, with restorations at the joins, now discolored.

Bibliography: Baur, *Stoddard Catalogue* 44–5, fig. 8; V. R. d'A. Desborough, *Protogeometric Pottery* (Oxford 1952) 8.

S. M. B.

8. Protogeometric Amphora

Attic. Ca. 1050–1000 B.C. *Stoddard Collection. Yale University Art Gallery 1913.50.*

The Protogeometric style represents an obvious continuation from the Submycenaean style exemplified by cat. no. 7. The shape and basic decorative format are consistent, although subtle differences of proportion and decorative motif already suggest the direction in which the Protogeometric and Geometric styles will develop. The Protogeometric artist places greater emphasis on the architectonic aspects of the vase. He raises the center of gravity to emphasize the shoulder and reinforces the gesture by the use of bold decoration. The appearance of concentric circles is an early example of a motif commonly found in Early and Middle Geometric pottery; the use of a compass and a multiple brush is a technical innovation of the Protogeometric. The motif probably derives ultimately from the degenerate spirals of Late and Submycenaean pottery. The decoration of this pottery consists mainly of bands, black and reserved, with concentric circles and semi-circles, although crosshatched triangles, lozenges and panels occur as well.

Protogeometric pottery was probably first made in Athens. Although local variants have been found in other sites in Greece, Crete, and the Cyclades, the changeover from the Submycenaean to this new form of pottery appears to have happened later at these sites than in Athens, and the stylistic impetus is clearly Athenian (V. R. d'A. Desborough, *The Last Mycenaeans and their Successors* [Oxford 1964] 263).

Cremation became the most popular form of burial in the period of transition from Late Sub-

7

8

mycenaean to Protogeometric and was the only form used for adults in Attica during the Protogeometric period. Neck-handled amphorae were commonly used as cinerary urns for male cremations and belly-handled amphorae frequently used for those of females in transitional graves, although some neck-handled vessels contained female ashes as well. By the Ripe and Late Protogeometric, neck-handles for men and belly-handles for women were universal.

V. R. d'A. Desborough (*Protogeometric Pottery* [Oxford 1952] 7–8) and C. G. Styrenius (*Submycenaean Studies* [Lund 1967] 63) place amphorae like this example in the transitional period. The closest parallels are those cited from the Kerameikos: PG grave A, inv. 522; PG grave 2, inv. 556; PG grave 25, inv. 915; and grave mound T7, inv. 591 (W. Kraiker and Karl Kübler, *Kerameikos* I [Berlin 1939] pls. 29, 56, 5 and 41 resp.).

Dimensions: H. 39.7 cm.

Description: Buff fabric with the glaze fired a deep brown. Two sets of compass-drawn concentric circles appear on the shoulder between the handles. Horizontal bands occur on the lip, below the shoulder decoration and on the lower body.

Condition: Neck and handles broken and mended with one missing piece restored. Restorations discolored.

Bibliography: Baur, *Stoddard Catalogue* 45, fig. 9; V. R. d'A. Desborough, *Protogeometric Pottery* (Oxford 1952) 8.

S. M. B.

GEOMETRIC POTTERY

Most of our knowledge of the Geometric period is based on pottery. No large-scale Geometric architecture, sculpture, or painting has been found to date. The style as we know it is readily adaptable to pottery and small objects. Pottery shapes seem to be intrinsically suggested, rather than derived from metal prototypes as was common in other times and places. A sense of form and proportion, a unity of decoration and shape were the primary objectives of the Geometric artist. A number of local variations of the Geometric style exist (J.N. Coldstream, *Greek Geometric Pottery* [London 1968] has isolated ten local styles) all within the basic Geometric idiom but distinctive in both shape and decoration.

The introduction of the human figure in identifiable scenes towards the end of the period is an important change for the development of later Greek pottery. The suitability of a vase for the representation of an heroic or ritual scene may have been accepted in the Geometric period as the only available substitute where monumental painting and sculpture were lacking. Once established, this use of the vase surface developed and continued until the fourth century B.C. when advances towards illusionism in painting went so far beyond the limits of a two color linear technique that vase painters reverted again to non-figured decoration.

Geometric pottery can be divided into a linear progression of three parts, of which only the late phase is represented in the Yale collection. The Late Geometric style explodes in an effusion of pattern. The overall system of decoration of these vessels is based on the multiplication of registers, completely transforming the restrained contrasting zones of the earlier styles into a tonally subdued tapestry effect. The first major proponent of this style was the Dipylon Master. This painter and his workshop were the originators of the monumental kraters and amphorae with funeral scenes that are our earliest surviving reflection of contemporary Greek life. The Dipylon workshop was large and its influence widespread.

The Dipylon style provides the basic context for all of Yale's Attic Geometric vessels; the pomegranate (cat. no. 9) and the tankard (cat. no. 10) are the closest in style to the Dipylon Workshop itself. The complex meander encircling the pomegranate is a typical Dipylon motif. Numerous hands have been isolated from surviving Late Geometric pottery (Jean Davison, *Attic Geometric Workshops* [New Haven 1961], and others). Among these the Bird Seed Painter, named for his use of parades of water birds with rows of dots ("bird seeds") is one of the more easily recognizable. Our standed bowl (cat. no. 11) adopts this motif, but cannot be demonstrated to belong to either the painter or his workshop.

Stylistic interchange is occasionally apparent. The Attic lekythos-oinochoe (cat. no. 12) virtually duplicates the shape of a Corinthian Late Geometric vessel (J.N. Coldstream, *Greek Geometric Pottery*, pl. 19d), with the exception of the handle, which is taller on the Attic version. That the shape is first Corinthian is demonstrated by its clear

9

development from Corinthian Middle Geometric beginnings (J.N. Coldstream, *Greek Geometric Pottery*, pl. 17g and 18c). The fabric of our vessel precludes a Corinthian origin.

The high standed bowl (cat. no. 13) shows both the degeneration of the style that characterized the end of Late Geometric and some new motifs more typical of the next stylistic phase, Protoattic. The rays, horizontal s-curves, and running wave pattern are frequently found on Protoattic vessels. The taller version of the normal Late Geometric standed bowl is symptomatic of Protoattic style as well. The trend throughout the Geometric towards taller and more elegant vessels reaches its extreme in the Protoattic.

9. Pomegranate Vase

Attic Geometric. Ca. 750–725 B.C. Stoddard Collection. Yale University Art Gallery 1913.60.

Dimensions: H. 10.2 cm.

Description: Vase in the shape of a pomegranate, open at the mouth. Buff fabric, glaze fired brown. Central wide band of complex meander between bands of crosshatched triangles and dotted lozenges, with checkerboard pattern around the mouth and bottom of the vase.

Condition: Two petals and part of a third missing from mouth, some surface pitting.

Bibliography: Baur, *Stoddard Catalogue* 51, fig. 11.

10. Olpe

Attic Geometric. 740–700 B.C. Stoddard Collection. Yale University Art Gallery 1913.55.

Dimensions: H. 17.6 cm.; D. of mouth 10 cm.

Description: Pinkish buff fabric (not Athenian, but possibly another Attic center: J.W. Hayes, orally, April, 1975), glaze fired dark brown. Bands of running dotted circles on the body, a single row of lozenges below the metopes on the broad neck. Three metopes separated by triglyphs with chevrons; two water birds with crosshatched bodies (swans?) flank the central metope of a circle of connected dotted circles within a large circle with rays.

Condition: Intact, but with some surface wear.

Bibliography: Baur, *Stoddard Catalogue* 49, fig. 11.

10

11

11. Standed Bowl

Attic Geometric. Ca. 725 B.C. Stoddard Collection. Yale University Art Gallery 1913.58.

Dimensions: H. 11.9 cm.; D. of mouth 17.9 cm.
Description: Buff fabric, glaze fired dark brown. Alternating panels of crosses and checkerboards on the stand, long panels of water birds with bird-seed rows in the handle zone; on the upper frieze two large panels of simple meander separated by metopes with a horse, checkerboard, and cross-hatched patterns.
Condition: Broken and repaired but unrestored. Considerable surface wear, especially on the stand.
Bibliography: Baur, *Stoddard Catalogue* 50, fig. 11.

12. Oinochoe

Attic Geometric. 740–700 B.C. Stoddard Collection. Yale University Art Gallery 1913.54.

Dimensions: H. 14.2 cm.
Description: Pinkish fabric, glaze fired black. Horizontal narrow bands around most of the body, chevrons and lozenges on the shoulder. On the neck four bands separated by double lines; in the bands dotted lozenges, vertical zig-zags and a lattice pattern. On the handle crosses separated by double lines.
Condition: Broken and repaired, lip chipped.
Bibliography: Baur, *Stoddard Catalogue* 48–9, fig. 11.

12

13

13. High Standed Bowl

Attic Late Geometric—Early Protoattic. 710–700 B.C. Stoddard Collection. Yale University Art Gallery 1913.59.

Dimensions: H. 19.8 cm. without lid, 25.6 cm. with lid; D. of mouth of bowl 16.6 cm.; D. of lid 16.5 cm.

Description: Buff fabric, glaze fired dark brown. Rays on the foot. Horizontal sss in the central band of the stand, two each between the triangular windows; vertical windows divide the rest of the stand into metopes which have horizontal zig-zag decoration. Bands on the bottom of the bowl, long panels of xxx and backwards NNN in the handle zone. A checkerboard pattern covers the upper part of the bowl. The lid is a series of friezes; from the outside: running wave pattern, horizontal sss, rays with swastikas between; rays on the knob handle. The lid seems to belong.

Condition: Foot broken and repaired, surface somewhat chipped.

Bibliography: Baur, *Stoddard Catalogue* 50–51, fig. 11.

S. M. B.

CORINTHIAN VASES

Homer mentions Corinth only once (*Iliad*, II.570), but the applied epithet *aphneios* (rich, wealthy) aptly characterizes that great commercial city, whose fortunate and strategic location a few miles southwest of the Isthmus afforded it control over both the only land routes linking the Peloponnesus with the Greek peninsula and over the sea traffic between the Corinthian Gulf (providing easy access to the western Greek colonies) and the Saronic Gulf (leading to the Aegean and eastern Mediterranean). From atop the rugged, towering height of Acrocorinth, at whose foot Old Corinth lies, the modern visitor may survey the immediate domain of the ancient city and sense the solid economic base for its once vast mercantile enterprise. Corinth stood at the hub of a wheel; many trade-routes radiated from the center or converged upon it. The Corinthian merchant—or at least the pottery that was the city's principal export—travelled to much of the known world: in the west, to Italy and its own colonies at Syracuse and Corcyra (founded, ancient sources tell us, around 734 B.C.), and in the east, to the Black Sea and Syria. It is not impossible that Corinthian traders at some time reached the Levant or that East Greek and Phoenician traders called at the two Corinthian ports of Lechaion (on the Corinthian Gulf) or Kenchreai (on the Saronic). Though the major commercial avenues lay to the west, it is likely that, in the earliest period of international trade, the foreign trader and Corinthian merchant bartered on intermediate islands in the Aegean, such as Thera, Crete, or Cyprus.

It is possible, then, that the story of Bellerophon, the only Homeric myth associated with Corinth (Homeric Ephyra; *Iliad* VI.152f.), reflects a specific historical circumstance: increased Greek and especially Corinthian contact with Eastern culture in the eighth and seventh centuries B.C. Driven from his homeland by the schemes of a lustful queen, Bellerophon went to Lycia (in what is now southern Turkey), and from there undertook victorious combats against a series of legendary foes: Amazons, the Solymoi, and the Chimaera," a divine creature not born of men, but a lion in front, a serpent behind, and a goat in the middle, breathing forth the might of blazing fire" (*Iliad*, VI. 180–2). To aid the hero in his adventures, Athena (according to Hesiod, Pindar, and later writers)

gave Bellerophon the means to capture and bridle the winged horse Pegasos, the offspring of still another fabulous creature, the Gorgon Medusa. Such hybrid beasts as these are Greek borrowings from the older cultures of the Orient. Pegasos, for example, may ultimately be derived from Assyrian, the Gorgon from Syrian, and the Chimaera from Neo-Hittite models. Other marvels—centaurs, sphinxes—enter Greek art towards the end of the eighth century, and remain an integral part of the vase painter's repertoire for centuries. An example of one of these hybrids, the siren (a bird's body with human head) is found on the large Middle Corinthian round aryballos (cat. no. 21, ca. 600–575 B.C.). Two large sirens flank a central ornament of lotus and palmette, perhaps the most common Corinthian floral motif. This and other ornaments, such as the solid rosette and the so-called "quatrefoil" pattern (which forms the sole decoration of the round aryballos, cat. no. 20), are also oriental in origin; most represent reworkings or debasements of Assyrian motifs.

It has often been assumed that Greek contact with the East, with its fantastic legends, monumental art, and established forms, finally broke the loosened bonds of the Geometric vision (which was, in any case, not as strong in Corinth as in Athens), and provided the stimulus for Greek pictorial and narrative art. If this view is correct, Greek art as a whole owes much to the Corinthian merchant and others like him, whose lively commerce not only imported foreign legends, ideas, models, and objects (perhaps textiles rather than vases) to the potter's and painter's workshop, but also supplied Corinthian goods to distant Greek outposts. First among those goods was, of course, pottery.

The most characteristic feature of the Corinthian vase is the fabric itself. Numerous clay beds in the Corinthia supplied the potter with an abundance of fine, whitish clay that, after firing, generally appears pale buff (a slightly green or pinkish tinge is not uncommon in certain periods). Corinthian ceramic can thus be distinguished at a glance from most other Greek fabrics, notably the redder Attic, with its higher iron oxide content.

The glaze varies in color, depending on the thickness of the paint, the consistency of application, and the firing process. When thickly applied, as on the small alabastron (cat. no. 17), the color is a uniform dark brown; but often, as on the large alabastron (cat. no. 19), the glaze is mottled, varying from brown to reddish.

The Corinthian painter deserves credit for a number of crucial technical innovations. The most outstanding of these is the black-figure technique, in which the painted silhouette is incised before firing with a sharp tool or stylus to render interior details or outlines. The process may be derived from metal work, such as the engraving of bronze. The earliest Corinthian piece with figures on display, the Late Protocorinthian piriform aryballos (cat. no. 16), contains an animal frieze with three running dogs, whose details are marked out with incisions that sometimes do not correspond to the painted form (for example, the incised curved tail and the traces of straight painted tail). Black-figure is dominant from the Protocorinthian period on. A more developed use of incision is found on the later, large alabastron (cat. no. 19); the incision of anatomical details on the lions and bird and the conventional cross-hatching of the lions' manes create a rich, active surface. Incision is also found on cat. nos. 17, 18, 21 and 22.

The black-figure technique is often accompanied by addition of colors, such as reddish-purple and white, which originally enhanced the decorative effect of the surface. But these colors tend to be far more fugitive than the dark glaze over which they were applied. The large alabastron (cat. no. 19) again is an exemplar of the technique: one can discern traces of purple used to accentuate areas around the eyes, shoulders, and bellies of the lions and the white dots that were applied to the chest of the bird and to the manes of the lions. Similarly, purple is found on the breasts, throats, and wings of the sirens on cat. No. 21 and is also used on cat. nos. 18 and 20.

The Stoddard collection contains a representative selection of vases illustrating the two principal periods of Corinthian vase painting: Protocorinthian (720–625 B.C.) and Corinthian (625–550 B.C.).

The most common Protocorinthian shapes are the kotyle (an example, 1913.71, is on display in the drinking cup section of the exhibition) and the aryballos, a small, narrow-mouthed vase that probably held perfumes or unguents. The sheer abundance of aryballoi at virtually all sites that have yielded Corinthian pottery to any degree perhaps indicates a Corinthian monopoly of the lucrative perfume trade, and gives credence to the Homeric phrase "luxurious Corinth". The changing proportions and contours of this simple shape, moreover, provide a relatively stable chronological sequence for the archaeologist. The earliest type is globular, represented in this collection by the Early

Protocorinthian cat. no. 14. Though the Geometric aesthetic has been rejected, the decoration of the aryballos is still abstract: reddish rings on the body and triangular, dark brown rays on the shoulder. In the Middle Protocorinthian period, the round body is attenuated into an ovoid form: cat. no. 15 is an example of the new shape. Its decoration retains the narrow rings and concentric circles but displays orientalizing ornaments on the shoulder: three hooked spirals and dot-rosettes. In the Late Protocorinthian period, the shape is attenuated still more; cat. no. 16 is an example of the pointed or piriform aryballos, barely able to stand on its own foot. The following Early Corinthian period brings with it a return to the round shape, as in cat. nos. 18 or 20. The new round aryballos can generally be distinguished from its Early Protocorinthian ancestor by its larger size (e.g. the big Middle Corinthian cat. no. 21, which needs a ring foot), and a wide, flat lip.

Though Protocorinthian vase painters could paint exquisite scenes of human action in a superbly executed miniaturist style (e.g. the famous "Chigi Vase" in the Villa Giulia, or the MacMillan Aryballos in London), the animal world, offering the opportunity for a pure, rich decorative art, remained the major component of Corinthian vases.

Among the favorite animals were boars, birds (particularly waterfowl; a swan is found on the back of cat. no. 21), goats (e.g. cat. no. 22), lions, and panthers. The depiction of certain creatures again suggests Oriental influence upon the Corinthian artist. In the Protocorinthian period, for example, a square-headed lion based on Hittite models is regular and is gradually replaced after 650 B.C. by the Assyrian type seen on the small Early Corinthian alabastron (cat. no. 17, where only the foreparts of an attacking lion and resisting bull are shown) and the large alabastron (cat. no. 19). Here two lions with cross-hatched manes heraldically confront a large, long-beaked bird of uncertain species. Such an antithetical composition is very common in Corinthian art.

The most common of all Corinthian animals is, however, the "panther"; no such animal exists in nature, but the term is loosely applied to any lion- or leopard-like cat with frontal head. The panther becomes extremely popular in Early Corinthian and virtually replaces lions completely by the second quarter of the sixth century. The Late Corinthian stemmed pyxis (cat. no. 22) illustrates the panther: on the front of the main zone,

15, 14, 16

two panthers heraldically flank four non-descript filling ornaments (buds?); on the back, there are two groups of a panther confronting a grazing goat. The entire frieze is covered with filling ornament of various kinds: rosettes, whirling rosettes, etc. It is a cluttered surface, as if the artist wanted to direct attention away from the rather careless draughtsmanship of the organic forms. The artist aims for a general decorative effect; no individual ornament could withstand close examination.

By the middle of the sixth century, the Corinthian animal style seems to have run its course. Athenian artists had in the meantime learned the lessons of Corinthian technique, ornament, and style. By around 600 B.C., Attic vase painting surpassed Corinthian in skill, and would soon surpass it in popularity. Superior clay, greater precision in draughtsmanship, and, above all, an inherent narrative impulse that led to the decoration of large surfaces with mythological scenes, contributed to the rise of Athenian pottery. Narrative scenes in Protocorinthian are fine but few; in Corinthian more common but somewhat less inspired. Corinthian art remained primarily dependent upon the animal style and the miniaturist style; both lost their appeal. Large-scale pictorial

and narrative art had been, however, at home in Athens since early in the seventh century. And, after a brief period of strong influence from the Corinthian animal style in the first quarter of the sixth century, the Athenian artist generally relegated the animal frieze to less important positions on the vase or did away with it entirely. At times, Corinthian vases tried to look Attic: a reddish slip is often aplied to the vase around 570–560 to imitate the Attic fabric. But the current of influence had dramatically changed course: Athenian vases effectively replaced Corinthian as the major pottery of Greek manufacture in the second quarter of the sixth century. After 550, Corinth ceases to be an important source of vase painting.

14. Round Aryballos

Early Protocorinthian. Ca. 720–690/680 B.C. Stoddard Collection. Yale University Art Gallery 1913.72.

Dimensions: H. 4.5 cm.; max. diam. 4.2 cm.
Description: Circle on underside of foot; rings of reddish hue on body; triangular rays on

20, 18, 17

shoulder, radiating from neck; circles on neck, lip, and around mouth. Vertical handle with horizontal stripes. Buff fabric; glaze ranges from brown to reddish.

Condition: Intact; paint flaking in areas.

Bibliography: Baur, *Stoddard Catalogue* 58, fig. 14.

15. Ovoid Aryballos

Middle Protocorinthian. Ca. 690–650 B.C. Stoddard Collection. Yale University Art Gallery 1913.73.

Dimensions: H. 6.5 cm.; max. diam. 4.2 cm.

Descrption: Buff fabric; foot glazed; two wide bands and twelve narrow rings on body; three hooked spirals, two dot-rosettes on shoulder; four concentric circles around mouth. Vertical handle with vertical stripe.

Condition: Lip repaired; pitted surface; some loss of glaze.

Bibliography: Baur, *Stoddard Catalogue* 58, fig. 14.

16. Piriform Aryballos

Late Protocorinthian. Ca. 650–640 B.C. Stoddard Collection. Yale University Art Gallery 1913.76.

Dimensions: H. 7.3 cm.; max diam. 3.8 cm.

Description: Buff fabric with brown paint; wide bands on and above foot; five narrow rings above and below frieze of three running dogs on body; wide band, three clusters of dots on shoulder; bands around lip and mouth; traces of horizontal lines on vertical handle.

Condition: Intact; surface pitted, with considerable loss of paint, lip chipped, crack in neck.

Bibliography: Baur, *Stoddard Catalogue* 59, fig. 14.

17. Alabastron

Early Corinthian. Ca. 625 B.C. Stoddard Collection. Yale University Art Gallery 1913.79.

Dimensions: H. 8.2 cm.; max. diam. 4.3 cm.

Description: Buff fabric, with dark brown paint; petal rosette on base; on body, foreparts of bull and foreparts of lion in confrontation; two incised rosettes on front, one solid rosette on rear; three short vertical lines on neck; dot frieze on rim of lip; on lip, six petals.

Condition: Intact; surface pitted in places, with loss of paint; lip chipped.

Bibliography: Baur, *Stoddard Catalogue 60*, fig. 14.

18. Round Aryballos

Early Corinthian. Ca. 625–600 B.C. Stoddard Collection. Yale University Art Gallery 1913.82.

Dimensions: H. 6 cm.; max. diam. 5.6 cm.

Description: Buff fabric painted dark brown; double incised lines radiating from neck to flat base, dividing surface into fifteen segments. Four segments covered with purple, three (apparently) with added white. Double incised lines also on lip, radiating from mouth.

Condition: Intact; some abrasion; some chips and cracks.

Bibliography: Baur, *Stoddard Catalogue 61*, fig. 14.

19. Alabastron

Middle Corinthian. Manner of the Painter of Louvre E 574. Ca. 600/590–580/575 B.C. Stoddard Collection. Yale University Art Gallery 1913.81.

Dimensions: H. 28.6 cm.

Description: Buff fabric with mottled glaze (brown to reddish); petal rosette on base, with three concentric rings; body devoted to heraldic composition of two lions around central bird; traces of added purple (around lions' eyes, shoulders, belly, on bird's beak), added white (on chest of bird, manes of lions); lions' tails intertwined on rear of vase; incised rosette between tail and mane of lion on left; petals and three bands on neck; dotted frieze on rim of lip; petals and concentric bands on lip.

Condition: Repaired from numerous pieces, considerable fading of glaze, especially on rear.

Bibliography: Baur, *Stoddard Catalogue 60–1*, fig. 14; J. L. Benson, "Some Notes on Corinthian Vase Painters" *AJA 60* (1956) 225, pl. 72, figs. 22–23.

19

20. Round Aryballos

Early Middle Corinthian. Probably after 600 B.C. Stoddard Collection. Yale University Art Gallery 1913.83.

Dimensions: H. 7 cm., max. diam. 6.8 cm.

21

22

Description: Buff fabric with dark brown paint, and added purple. Bands on lip and around mouth; "quatrefoil" ornament (four purple petals, with netted interstices, lotus below) forms sole decoration on body.

Condition: Intact; some chips and cracks; occasional paint loss.

Bibliography: Baur, *Stoddard Catalogue* 83, fig. 14.

21. Large Round Aryballos

Middle Corinthian. Ca. 600–575 B.C. *Stoddard Collection. Yale University Art Gallery 1913.88.*

Dimensions: H. 14.8 c.m., max. diam. 14.2 cm.

Description: Buff fabric with brown and traces of purple paint; ring foot with concentric bands; on front of body, two sirens flanking a central lotus and palmette ornament; on rear, a very faded waterfowl; small incised rosettes and dots sprinkled over body frieze; large rosettes on rear. Added purple on breasts, throat, and wings of sirens. On shoulder, petals and row of dots; dots on rim of lip; petals and concentric bands around mouth.

Condition: Lip repaired; occasional stress cracks below handle; paint extremely faded on rear and on much of front; much surface abrasion.

Bibliography: Baur, *Stodard Catalogue* 63.

22. Stemmed Pyxis

Late Corinthian. By the Geladakis Painter. End of the Sixth Century B.C. *Stoddard Collection. Yale University Art Gallery 1913.101.*

Dimensions: H. 25 cm., with handles.

Description: Buff fabric, with paint hue ranging from brown to reddish; a frieze of six wild, grazing goats on stem; main frieze on belly contains two panthers flanking four "buds"; on rear, two groups of a panther confronting a grazing goat; field cluttered with many incised rosettes, dots, blotches.

Condition: Stem broken and repaired; paint worn and faded.

Bibliography: Baur, *Stoddard Catalogue* 68, fig. 14; J. L. Benson, "Some Notes on Corinthian Vase Painters" *AJA* 60 (1956) 229, pl. 77, fig. 41 (attribution to Geladakis Painter).

J. H.

NON-ATTIC WARES

Most of the vases in this exhibition exemplify developments in Attic vase painting, but Attica was not the only geographical district of Greece to manufacture her own pottery. There were many other pottery workshops on the mainland, the islands, and the Ionian (Asia Minor) coast. Findspot is not always the key to the correct attribution of a vase's provenance. The fabric of a vase (its clay type) and the stylistic features of its shape and decoration are important factors in deducing the place of manufacture.

Provincial schools often directly imitated or were influenced by the mainstream Attic styles; yet, native local tastes and traditions in pottery production persisted both in their pure forms and as hybrids. Boeotian, North Ionian, and Rhodian vases in the Yale collection illustrate this tendency to incorporate Attic ceramic fashions with the indigenous styles of those areas outside of Attica.

The earliest example on display of a non-Attic Geometric ware is the trefoil-mouthed oinochoe (cat. no. 23) made in Boeotia. This vase dates to ca. 720–700 B.C. and belongs to the Boeotian Late Geometric period; yet, it was influenced by styles of the Attic Late Geometric I period, which is dated to ca. 760–735 B.C. It is not uncommon, as the present case reveals, for provincial fashions to lag behind those of Attica in chronological development, but the determination of the precise time lag is difficult. While Atticizing features such as architectonic divisions of the decoration with emphasis on the neck, shoulder, and belly of the vase, the use of neck metopes (panels), and the use of crosshatched triangles are employed here, this oinochoe also exhibits typically Boeotian features: rows of concentric circles and the lines framing the filling ornaments on the neck.

A characteristic shape produced in great quantities throughout the seventh century B.C. by several variant workshops, on the Ionian coast and the islands, is the so-called "Rhodian Bird Bowl." Cat. no. 24 is an example of this group. The toponym "Rhodian" is used regardless of the place of manufacture since the initial appearance of this vase type was probably on Rhodes where its shape and decoration seem to have evolved from a Rhodian Late Geometric kotyle (cup) form. Our bowl is not of Rhodian manufacture; its fabric indicates a North Ionian provenance. Since the upper field of our pot is decorated in a debased Geometric style,

it belongs to the Subgeometric period and more specifically to the later part of this period, ca. 620–600 B.C. This is evidenced by the disc foot and void rays on the lower body, which are among the later stylistic features of the shape. The void rays on this form are, in fact, part of the repertoire of the succeeding Orientalizing period.

The style of the Orientalizing period includes many floral motifs derived from the Near East such as the palmette motif on the rim of Side B of the Boeotian kantharos, cat. no. 25. The birds of Side A are local in character and are distinctive of a series of Boeotian cups with this motif. This class of pottery is called the "Bird Cup Group." It begins ca. 560 B.C. and ends ca. 480 B.C. Our kantharos is early in the series, perhaps ca. 550 B.C. Local also is the shape of this kantharos, which developed from a Boeotian Late Geometric kantharos form. The use of a slip, here a white overcoat of clay intended to enhance the surface color and texture of the vase, and the use of an added red paint are Boeotian features rarely found in Attic wares.

The influence of the Attic black-figure style is indirectly reflected, however, in the Yale neck amphora, cat. no. 26. This black-figure piece is probably of Rhodian manufacture. Its stylistic affinities to the British Museum amphora *BMC* B. 21, which is purported to come from Camirus on Rhodes, led J.D. Beazley to attribute both these vases to the same painter (*Etruscan Vase-painting*, [Oxford 1947] 14). (Dietrich von Bothmer believes that the Metropolitan Museum of Art amphora published in *The Metropolitan Museum of Art Bulletin* 8 [1949] 93–94 belongs to this class of vases). Although the Yale and British Museum amphorae are probably Rhodian, they are dependent upon the Clazomenian black-figure style of the second half of the sixth century B.C. Clazomenian is a North Ionian school which was influenced by the Attic black-figure style.

The use of a row of scales framing drops above a row of dots on the upper border of the two main panels is a Clazomenian feature. So too is the lion of Side A, which is similar to a lion on a Clazomenian sarcophagus in Dresden (#1643, *BSA* 47, 140, fig. 6). The profile of this vase is close to neck amphorae of the Knipovitch class of pottery, which is related to Clazomenian. The orange-brown reserved background recalls the orange surface color of Attic black-figure wares. Also, the arrangement of the fields, with individual motifs (here the animals) in the main panels and the abstract in subsidiary fields, is Attic in origin.

23. Oinochoe

Boeotian. Ca. 720–700 B.C. *Stoddard Collection. Yale University Art Gallery 1913.52.*

Dimensions: H. 37.8 cm.

Description: No foot. Globular body reaches maximum diameter below mid-height. Vertical sloping shoulder, short neck, trefoil mouth. Wide strap handle vertically set below at the base of the shoulder and above at the lip. Interior: plain. Exterior: reserved background except for solid black-glazed mouth, base, and two broad zones around the lower body which are separated by a narrow reserved circumference band. On the neck five metopes framed above by two concentric circumference bands and below by three circumference bands, and each laterally framed by two parallel vertical lines. The central metope has eight horizontal parallel zig-zag lines, the upper line with dots. The two flanking metopes are each composed of a central lozenge flanked by lateral triangles whose apices are tangent to the lateral apices of the lozenge. Each of these forms encloses a smaller cross-hatched replica of itself. In the field there are four crosshatched pendent triangles, two above and two below. The next metope has three vertical parallel zig-zag lines. The last metope is solid black. On the shoulder a horizontal zig-zag circumference line above a narrow concentric circumference band; below a row of nine sets of six compass drawn, concentric circles each with central dot and interrupted by three parallel vertical lines and the handle. On the upper body is a horizontal zig-zag line framed above and below by a set of three concentric circumference bands. On the mid-body are a row of sixteen sets of six concentric circles each with central dot and interrupted by three parallel vertical lines. Below is a horizontal zig-zag line framed above by three concentric circumference bands and below by six. On the surface of the strap handle are black parallel horizontal lines, crosshatched where handle arches to meet lip. Edges black-glazed, underside reserved.

Condition: Complete, mended from many fragments. Rather coarse, hard, orange-brown clay with particles of mica. Dull black glaze fired rust, red, and brown.

Bibliography: Baur, *Stoddard Catalogue* no. 52, p. 47, fig. 11; J.N. Coldstream, *Greek Geometric Pottery* (London 1968) 201; closest parallel Sam Wide, *JdI* 14 (1899) 83, fig. 39; cf. also Fulvio Canciani, *JdI* 80 (1965) 67, fig. 19; *CVA* Copenhagen plate 67, 3.

24. Bird Bowl

North Ionian. Ca. 620–600 B.C. *Stoddard Collection. Yale University Art Gallery 1913.65.*

Dimensions: H. 8.3 cm.; D. rim 16.4 cm.; D. base 4.1 cm.

Description: Low disc foot depressed at center, widely flaring body walls create deep bowl, slightly convex rim. Two horizontally set loop handles attached beneath the rim. Interior: black-glazed except for reserved central disc at the base and a reserved band at mid-height; three added white-red-white lines in sets. Exterior: background reserved. Foot black-glazed fired rust to black. Above the inset of the foot circumference band and five void rays pointed upwards. The points extend beyond the three concentric circumference bands

24

at mid-body which on one side merge into one broad band. Handle zone on both sides divided into three metopes by four sets of vertical lines in groups of three. Central metope: bird facing right with crosshatched, drop-shaped body and two double-pronged legs. In the field: above the bird's back is a pendent triangle, to the right two arcs around one dot each, one above the head and the other below its feet. Each flanking metope filled with a crosshatched lozenge within a lozenge. Handles flanked by one vertical line on each side. Lip and exterior of handles black-glazed.

Condition: Complete, mended from five fragments. Ridges on exterior of body which may be an accident of firing. Hard fine brownish-buff clay with particles of mica. Black glaze, added red and white paints.

Bibliography: Baur, *Stoddard Catalogue* 53, no. 65, fig. 16; closest parallel Giulio Jacopi, *Clara Rhodos* 6–7 (1933) 54 fig. 61; cf. also K.F. Kinch, *Fouilles de Vroulia* (1941), col. 50, pl. 42, t. 18.2; Georges Vallet and François Villard, *Mégara Hyblaea* 2 (1964) pl. 63, 1–2; general: J.N. Coldstream, *Greek Geometric Pottery* (London 1968) 298–301; M.F. Lambrino, *Les Vases Archaïques d' Histria* (Bucharest 1938) 39–46.

25. Kantharos

Greek. Boeotian. Ca. 550 B.C. Stoddard Collection. Yale University Art Gallery 1913.178.

Dimensions: H. to rim 17.1 cm.; H. to top of handles 21 cm.; D. rim 17.3 cm.; D. base 8.3 cm.

Description: Low ring foot, deep body with convex flaring walls, narrow sloping shoulder, offset and outturned wide rim. Two vertically set high-swung strap handles attached below to the shoulder and above to the lip. Interior: white slipped background upon which two black-glazed bands on the rim, two on the body, and a black disc, bottom center, are superimposed. Exterior: white slipped background. Foot black-glazed, underside four concentric black-glazed rings and a black central disc at the base. Lower body, six concentric black circumference bands; mid-body, two horizontal wavy bands separated by a black concentric circumference band; upper body, two black-glazed concentric circumference bands. On the shoulder, a row of black, short and parallel, vertical strokes above which is a black ring. Side A: two birds with outstretched wings fly right. Details of shoulders, wings, and eyes in added red. To the right of each bird a cross-hatched vertical

panel, in the field a dot rosette above the head of each bird and a crosshatched triangle below. A pair of horizontal S-curves frame each tail. Side B: two metopes framed by three crosshatched panels slanting upwards from left to right and increasing in width from right to left. Each metope has a palmette with nine alternating black and red petals stemming from a crosshatched lozenge center beneath which is a double volute upon the apex of a crosshatched triangle. The volute on the right extends upward and forms a single volute on the upper rim. In the lower field of each metope is a crosshatched triangle. Black glaze and added red

paint applied to the lip. Handles are edged in black glaze and have parallel horizontal lines; the undersides are plain, rather coarse, hard, brownish-buff clay with particles of mica. White slip, dull black glaze, and added red paint.

Condition: Intact; glaze peeling.

Bibliography: Baur, *Stoddard Catalogue*, no. 178, pp. 115–116, fig. 16; cf. Johannes Boehlau, *JdI* 3 (1888) 334, fig. 6 for the bird motif and p. 339, fig. 15 for shape and palmette motif; *CVA* München, Museum Antiker Kleinkunst, 6, pl. 270, 1–2 for shape and bird motif; general: R.M. Burrows and P.N. Ure, *BSA* 14 (1908) 226–318.

26. Neck Amphora

Greek, probably Rhodian. Last third of the sixth century B.C. *Stoddard Collection. Yale University Art Gallery 1913.230.*

Dimensions: H. 32.4 cm.

Description: Flaring ring foot depressed at center with a flat resting surface supports a wide ovoid body which reaches its maximum diameter above mid-height. Concave vertical sloping shoulder, short neck, offset and outward thickened angular rim with flat lip. Two vertically set loop handles, round in section, attached below at the base of the shoulder and above at the neck. Interior: plain except for black-glazed lip and rim. Exterior: foot black-glazed. Lower body, panel on each side, and underside of handles reserved. Remaining areas black-glazed. On the neck are three meanders, two of which are connected; a black band below; on the shoulder a row of eight drops each framed by a horseshoe-shaped line left open at the top, below a row of dots. The main field of the body on each side has one animal. Side A: lion crouching to left, right forepaw and haunches raised, gaping mouth, protruding tongue, curving tail. Incision for the nose, whiskers, eyes, ear, fur, claws, stomach, legs, and haunches. Side B: stag with body facing left and head turned looking over his back. Front of body crouching, haunches raised. Squiggle for tail. Mouth open, right forepaw raised. Eye, mouth, stomach, ears, and horns incised. Coarse clay, highly micaceous with white incisions. Fired light brown. Dull black glaze fired rust to brown. Incision.

Condition: Intact; surface chipped.

Bibliography: Baur, *Stoddard Catalogue,* no. 230, p. 140, fig. 52a and b; J.D. Beazley, *Etruscan Vase-painting* (Oxford 1947) 14; Dietrich von Bothmer, *Metropolitian Museum of Art Bulletin* 8 (1949) 93–94; closest parallel: *CVA British Museum* 8, p. 38, pl. 1, 1 and 2; cf. also Boris Pharmakowsky, *JdI* 27 (1912) 334–335, figs. 20–21; general: J. M. Cook, *BSA* 60 (1965) 114–142; R.M. Cook, *BSA* 47 (1952) 123–152.

L. J. S.

26, Side A

26, Side B, detail

27

BLACK-FIGURE VASES

27. Black-Figure Loutrophoros

Attic. 600–575 B.C. *Stoddard Collection. Yale University Art Gallery 1913.104.*

Early Attic vase painting was heavily influenced by Corinthian ware, as can be seen in this loutrophoros. Generally speaking, however, the impulse in Athens is to subdue and simplify the inherited decorative vocabulary, and less interest is shown in the elaborate polychromy and dense filling ornament of Corinthian ware. For example, the bands which separate the friezes of animals in Corinthian vases are composed of a series of heavy parallel lines, sometimes with checked patterns. But in Attic vases, such as this loutrophoros, these are simplified into a single thin line, giving the animals much more space in which to circulate.

Early Attic black-figure vases of this type are often characterized by a freedom of incision not found in their Corinthian counterparts until the last phases of the decline of the animal style. In the Yale loutrophoros, the incision is rough and often extends considerably beyond the painted contours of the animal, suggesting a greater interest in the silhouette of the animal as a flat decorative form, rather than the precise segmented articulation of the body.

Athenian artists also elaborate the iconography of the animal style by adding sphinxes and sirens, both of which are derived from Eastern sources. Although they occur occasionally in Corinthian ware, they are found far more frequently in Attic pottery, perhaps because their heraldic quality makes them easily adaptable to symmetrical compositions. The palmette lotus motif is also an important decorative element in Attic black-figure. Although it appears on Corinthian vases, the motif acquires a new complexity and prominence in Athenian vase painting, where it is used as a central organizational element.

Although this vase has been atributed to Sophilos (Benson), it belongs rather to a broader animal style which flourished in Athens during the first quarter of the sixth century. The flaccid and elongated bodies of the animals, and the roughness of the incision, suggest that this vase may be a rather late example.

Dimensions: H. 29 cm.; D. 15.2 cm.

Description: Conical foot and ring above it fired solid red, as are the rays encircling the lower third of the body. Animal friezes divided by single bands, also fired red. Below the neck, alternating black and red tongue pattern. Reddish fabric with whitish slip. Red: tongues, stripes on panthers' bodies, birds' wings, sphinx's haunch, dots on wings of the harpie to the right of the sphinx, and ring at the base of the neck. White: sphinx's face and chest, and dots on her wings.

Condition: Broken and repaired. The upper parts of the vase are the most severely damaged: all of the neck and handles are missing, as well as one half of the upper frieze of animals and one third of the lower frieze. The surface is somewhat damaged by blisters, and the white on the faces of the sirens and sphinxes has been lost. Application of the glaze in an excessively thin solution accounts for the mottled reddish quality of the surface.

Bibliography: Baur, *Stoddard Catalogue* 70–71, fig. 16; J. L. Benson, "Some Notes on Corinthian Vase Painters," *AJA* 60 (1956) 226. On Sophilos, see J. D. Beazley, *The Development of Attic Black-Figure Vase Painters* (Oxford 1951) 17–19; and John Boardman, *Athenian Black-Figure Vases* (London 1974) 18–19, figs. 24–48 with bibliography.

C. B.

28. Black-Figure Hydria

Attic. Attributed to the Polos Group. Ca. 580–560 B.C. Stoddard Collection. Yale University Art Gallery 1913.105.

The Polos Group, Attic in origin and characterized by distinctive crosshatched pill-box shaped hats worn by sirens and sphinxes, consists of approximately one hundred and sixty pots and fragments. The prototype for the ornamentation of the Polos Group is the animal style of Corinthian pottery, with its systematic rendering of sirens, lions, sphinxes, and birds. Incised rosettes of varying size repeated in the field around the animals are set within the confines of parallel bands to establish a unity of design. The combined use of areas of black paint highlighted with purple and defined by incised lines, a black neck band, and a base band of projecting black rays, are all elements repeated by the Polos Group. The Corinthian prototypes, however, are distinguishable from their Attic descendants by the fine texture and pale cream-colored clay characteristic of Corinth. Similarly, as noted by Humfry Payne and R. M. Cook, the Polos Group seems at best imitative and derivative, lacking the spirit of conviction evident in Corinthian models.

Other Polos-type pots are readily identifiable, yet it is more difficult to determine with any certainty the hand of a particular painter since the debased quality of the genre obscures the style of the individual artist. While there has been some disagreement in the past about whether the Polos-type pots were the work of a single painter or of a group of painters, close examination indicates the latter view to be more acceptable. A comparison of the Yale hydria to an amphora at the British Museum (London B 18 [Beazley, *ABV* 44, no. 1]) and

28

a hydria at the Museum of Fine Arts, Boston (Boston 76.34 [Beazley, *ABV* 44, no. 19]) is representative of the degree of variation in painting technique found in the Polos Group. Both the London amphora and the Boston hydria indicate that the painter or painters of these vessels are especially concerned with spacing of figures and delineation of detail. Where the sphinxes and panthers on the Yale hydria seem cramped within their bands and have clumsily ovoid-shaped features, the lions on London B 18 and Boston 76.34 possess more attenuated bodies and extended tails.

The most curious motif on this pot is the central element between the two confronted sphinxes on Side A. It ultimately derives from the elaborate double lotus motif commonly found on Corinthian animal style pots. All that seems to remain is a crude columnar abstraction of two lotus blossoms which appear in varying states of simplification on a number of other examples of the Polos Group.

The form of the hydria, with its vertical side handles and its extended trumpet-shaped neck is somewhat unusual. This neck shape is a characteristic not found in Corinth in the sixth century, but it appeared in Attica as early as the Protoattic period and is seen in several short-lived amphora-shaped hydriae.

Polos-type fragments and pots have been discovered at varied locations including Delos, Naukratis, Rhodes, and Cervetri, but the greatest number have been unearthed at Athens. This distribution of the pots suggests that while Attica was the source for the Polos Group it found a ready market overseas. Further, the general crudity of the Polos Group and the great number of extant examples implies that the wares were mass-produced.

Dimensions: H. 21.06 cm.

Description: Reddish fabric, incision used extensively for details in black areas. Red: Sphinxs' wings, panthers' shoulder and heads, harpies' wings and hair, necks of birds by back handle, rosettes in top register and one in the field. Side A: Six bands of decoration, uppermost being a simple black border below lip, beneath which runs a band of rosettes. Lower neck band depicts two sphinxes flanking a siren with its wings spread and the background filled with rosettes of varying size. On shoulder band two confronted sphinxes flank an abstraction of the double lotus motif, the lower lotus blossom being inverted. Lower figural band contains two confronted panthers, their heads turned full face. The bottom band consists of projecting rays. Side B: Upper and lower bands

repeat Side A. Neck band depicts rear portions of the two sphinxes which flank siren on Side A. Shoulder band: two headlines birds with rosettes in background. Lower figural band: two sphinxes confronted and rosettes used as filling for background.

Condition: Repaired but complete, except for one minor wedge-shaped loss on the lower body; slight chipping and abrasion on lip; areas of paint loss on base band of rays, foot, and long vertical handle connecting shoulder and upper part of neck.

Bibliography: Baur, *Stoddard Catalogue* 71–2, fig. 16. On the Polos Group: Beazley, *ABV* 43–9; R. M. Cook, *Greek Painted Pottery* (London 1972) 79; Elvira Folzer, *Die Hydria* (Leipzig 1906) 50–51; Payne, *NC* 190–91; Hermann Thiersch, '*Tyrrhenische*' *Amphoren* (Leipzig 1899) 146.

R. S.

29. Black-Figure Komast Cup

Attic. Attributed to the KY Painter. Ca. 580–570 B.C. Stoddard Collection. Yale University Art Gallery 1913.102.

On both Sides A and B, three padded dancers step briskly in three defined poses, the central figure holding a rhyton. These padded dancers have been identified as komasts, a favorite subject in Corinth since the seventh century B.C., and included in the Attic repertory during the sixth century B.C. A typical padded dancer appears in profile view wearing a sleeveless chiton, with padding on the buttocks and shoulder rings for ribbons. Corinthian komast dancers are usually male, nude, or padded; on Late Ripe Corinthian vases these dancers are often accompanied by women, and later still, in the Attic tradition, padded and chitoned women become very frequent (see the tripod-kothon in the manner of the KY Painter in the National Museum, Athens, 12688, dating ca. 575–55 B.C. Beazley, *ABV* 33, no. 1). The stockiness of the komasts on this cup is characteristic of a Corinthian type, since from ca. 560 or 550 B.C. onwards slender, nude Attic komasts gradually displace the typical Corinthian padded dancer on Attic Komast vases. The Attic dancers inherit few of the elaborate settings surrounding the Corinthian komasts: the latter usually hold rhyta, dance around wine-kraters, steal wine in comic scenes, are accompanied by padded-musicians, and in general are riotous and

29

frenzied in their behavior. In contrast, the Attic dancers appear as more isolated figures with only three fixed stances: either parallel feet, or one leg lifted in front, or one leg kicked up behind. Bearded and unbearded types mingle in both Corinthian and Attic scenes: on this cup, all three komasts of Side B are young, while Side A presents a bearded dancer facing two youthful komasts.

Although the komast dancer is defined as a member of the komos, a group singing and dancing after a symposion, scholars have also linked the komast with Dionysiac ritual, with satyrs and satyr-plays, and hence with the pre-dramatic origins of tragedy. The dance of the komasts itself appears to have no supernatural, divine, or dramatic significance. Padded dancers, however, do seem to have been associated in pre-dramatic times with the antecedents of both tragedy and comedy. They are related to satyrs and Dionysos; they appear in pre-dramatic comic scenes; and their padded costume was perpetuated in Attic comedy down to the fourth century B.C. Padded dancers and komasts appeared also in the plastic arts, as in terracotta and bronze figurines.

The Attic Komast cups had long been considered Corinthian in origin, until several scholars cor-

rectly identified the fabric of the group as Attic (see Adolf Greifenhagen, 1929; Payne, NC; J. D. Beazley, Hesperia, 13 [1944]). Although its rich orange-red clay points to an Attic origin, the Yale Komast cup is exemplary of the eclectic borrowing of Corinthian elements in early sixth century B.C. Attica. This borrowing of Corinthian features in Attic pottery occurred both in shape and in decoration. The seventh and sixth century Corinthian cup is full and round, compared with the sudden angular recession of the bowl in the Attic cup, which is much shallower. The Attic cup possesses a concave lip and short, stubby handles. The Attic Komast cup is characteristized by the flat and horizontal projection of its handles, and its striking departure from the heavy and full-bodied Corinthian cup. In the subsidiary decoration of the Yale Komast cup, the lotus-and-palmette ornaments under the handles form a very common Corinthian motif.

The attribution of this cup to the KY Painter by J. D. Beazley (ABV 32 no. 16) is assured, in view of his distinctive style: particularly consistent are his very lively and spontaneous drawing, his depiction of bulky dancers with bulbous padding, and his adherence to the three fixed komast stances. Notable also is the KY Painter's continuous use of long, sloping noses and of hands lacking incisions (like gloves). Most characteristic is his manner of incising the feet with three to four parallel lines. The Yale cup belongs to the Attic black-figure Komast Group of vases, of which the KX Painter is the chief painter. Named for the frequent appearance of komasts, revellers, and padded dancers on their vases, the Komast Group produced vase shapes of all kinds, from lekanides to column-kraters. The first letter in the monograms assigned to the KX and the KY Painters refers to the komast, the subject matter of the majority of their vases. The KY Painter introduced the column-krater into the Attic repertory of vase-shapes, but more than two-thirds of the vases attributed to him are cups. On vases other than cups, the artists of the Komast Group continued many Corinthian conventions, such as animal friezes of opposing sphinxes and panthers. All the vases of the Komast Group are made of fine red Attic clay and are of high technical quality. When Athens began to be successful in her commercial competition with Corinth, they appear to have been exported from Attica all over the Greek world.

Dimensions: H 8.7 cm.; D. 19.3 cm.

Description: Handles, exterior of foot, and interior of cup all painted black; inner sides of the handles reserved. Incision work sloppy, not following the contours of the black paint: only parts of the ornament are incised. The untidy quality of the incised lines would seem to indicate a hurried, and perhaps massive, workshop decoration of Komast cups. Incision work on rosettes, lotus-and-palmettes, tendrils, figures. Red: rim—alternating petals of rosettes; handle sides—alternating petals of lotus-and-palmettes, and lotus kalyx; Sides A and B—padded suits of the dancers, and alternating petals of rosettes.

Condition: Broken and repaired with little damage to the decoration; no restoration. Sides A and B: black glaze flaked off the bodies of the dancers; handles and especially Side A abraded. Parts of rim and interior misfired. Applied red worn, especially on the padded suits of the dancers.

Bibliography: Baur, *Stoddard Catalogue* 69, no. 102; J. D. Beazley, *Hesperia* 13 (1944) 48, no. 13, and *ABV* 32, no. 16; Adolf Greifenhagen, *Eine attische schwarzfigurige Vasengattung und die Darstellung des Komos im VI Jahrhundert* (Königsberg 1929), no. 5; On the Komast Group, see Payne, *NC* 194 no. 7, Axel Seeberg, "Corinthian Komos Vases," *Bulletin Supplement* Institute of Classical Studies, London, no. 27, 1971; J. D. Beazley, "Groups of Early Attic Black-figure," *Hesperia* 13 (1944) 38–57, and *The Development of Attic Black-Figure* (Berkeley 1951); on the komast or padded dancer, see A. W. Pickard-Cambridge, *Dithyramb, Tragedy, and Comedy* (Oxford 1962, 2nd edition, revised by T. B. L. Webster).

M. M. B.

30. Black-Figure Tripod Pyxis

Attic. Ca. 560–540 B.C. Stoddard Collection. Yale University Art Gallery 1913.122.

Side A shows Achilles pursuing Troilos, an early episode in the Trojan War. According to an oracle, Troy could not be taken if Troilos, the youngest son of the Trojan King Priam, reached his twentieth year. In order to prevent such a disastrous outcome to the war for the Greeks, Achilles hid by the fountain outside the city to ambush Troilos when he came to water his horses. On seeing Achilles attacking, Troilos fled on horseback toward the altar of Apollo, hoping for the protection of the sanctuary. Troilos' sister Polyxena, who had accompanied her brother to the fountain on foot, also fled, dropping her hydria in the panic of the escape. Achilles overtook Troilos at the altar of Apollo and slew him on the altar itself. This violation of Apollo's sanctuary ended ultimately in Achilles' death at the hand of Paris, aided by Apollo himself.

The Troilos episode comes not from the *Iliad*, where Troilos is mentioned only once as dead (XXIV,257), but from a later epic poem, the *Cypria*, which sets out the events leading up to the point where the *Iliad* begins. The *Cypria* is lost, but Achilles' pursuit of Troilos survives in the *Aeneid* of Virgil (I, 474) and in a substantial number of pictorial representations. These may be broken up into four groups, each showing a different part of the myth: 1) Achilles lying in wait at the fountain, 2) Achilles pursuing Troilos, 3) the murder on the altar and 4) the fight over the body. The first two are by far the most common. The subject was a popular one on both black and red-figure vases, part of a large group of Trojan War episodes drawn from the *Iliad, Odyssey* and *Iliupersis* (Sack of Troy) as well as the *Cypria*. The pursuit scene usually includes Achilles, armed, with drawn sword and Corinthian helmet; Troilos, mounted on one horse and often leading another; Polyxena,

30, Side A

30, Side B

30, Side C

with her hydria somewhere on the ground, and the fountain, to set the scene. Athena, who encourages Achilles in this deed, and other subsidiary figures are sometimes included, as in the François Vase by Kleitas (Florence Museo Archeologico 4209, John Boardman, *Athenian Black Figure Vases* [London 1974] fig. 46.5, etc.), but the most basic figures are those on the Yale pyxis. More abbreviated forms occur as well, showing only an armed warrior pursuing a youth on horseback, but these do not so obviously refer to the Troilos myth. Polyxena's unbroken hydria is probably meant to be bronze (Mario del Chiaro, "Classical Vases in the Santa Barbara Museum of Art," *AJA* 68 [1964] 107). The onlooker on the far left is not an identifiable part of the episode.

Male courting scenes involving an older man and a young boy (Erastes and Eromenos, Side B) were a common subject on Attic vases. J.D. Beazley (*Some Attic Vases in the Cyprus Museum* [London 1949] 7–31) distinguishes three types, representing three stages in the progress of the courtship. In the earliest of the three, the man faces the boy (the boy usually facing left) and caresses him in an expectant or entreating way. As in the present example, the man's knees are normally bent and his arms in the "up and down" position. The boy often, as here, grasps the man's wrists. Frequently the two main figures are flanked by onlookers, who sometimes dance and/or encourage the participants. Beazley's second and third types show more advanced stages of the courtship. In the second type the man presents the boy with a gift, often a cock or a rabbit (see cat. no. 53). The third type shows the figures interlocked.

On Side C a peplos-clad woman stands in the center, flanked by two men in himatia and two nude youths. The woman is veiled, but holds the veil out from her face. The man standing behind her holds a spear. The meaning of the scene is unclear. The woman's gesture normally means "wife of," but it can have connotations of despair; it is commonly used by Helen in representations of her return to Menelaos after the end of the Trojan War. As Menelaos is normally shown bearded and armed, often with sword drawn and almost always grasping Helen's wrist, this scene cannot be implied here. Nor, presumably, is it a wedding scene, as the woman's attendants are all male, and one holds a spear.

The shape originates in Middle Corinthian (Payne, *NC* 308) and is confined to the sixth century in Attica. The transition from the Corinthian kothon shape to the Attic form of the present example carries through the work of the Polos Group (580–570 B.C., see cat no. 28), the KY Painter (570–560 B.C., see cat. no. 29) and the C Painter (575–555 B.C.) and ends with a group of unattributed examples around 540 B.C. The Yale pyxis shows some influence of Lydos (active around 560–540 B.C.), particularly in the bandage stripes of some of the himatia, and is probably contemporary with the work of that artist.

Dimensions: H. 8.1 cm.; D. 14.8 cm.

Description: Red. Side A: shoulder and lowest sections of the himation worn by the onlooker, Achilles' helmet, the horse's tail, Polyxena's fillet and peplos, except for the center panel of the skirt; Side B: the himatia of the two outermost on-lookers, the hair of all but the figure on the extreme left, wreaths held by the two central figures; Side C: (figures numbered from left to right) the hair on figure 1, the bands of the himation worn by figure 2, the skirt and part of the veil worn by figure 3, the himation and hair of figure 4, the hair of figure 5, and a narrow band around the lip on the interior and exterior. White: Side A: the short tunic worn by Troilos, Polyxena's flesh; Side B: possibly dots on the wreath around the arm of the youth; Side C: flesh of the central figure (3), possibly traces remaining of dotted circles on the veil worn by the same figure and on the himation worn by figure 4, and on the dotted neck border of the himation worn by figure 4.

31

Condition: Lid missing. Broken and repaired, but not restored. Black glaze badly worn; it is best preserved where added white originally covered it, and on the interior of the bowl. The figure on the extreme left on Side B is almost totally lost.

Bibliography: Baur, *Stoddard Catalogue* 82, pl. 3,4; Charline Hofkes-Brukker, *Frühgriechische Gruppenbildung* (Leiden and Würzburg, 1935) pl. 5,11; J.D. Beazley, *Some Attic Vases in the Cyprus Museum* (London 1947) 5 and 8; Münzen und Medaillen, Basel, catalogue Auction 40, 13 December 1969, p. 36; Brommer, *Vasenlisten* 361.

S. M. B.

31. Black-Figure Lekythos

Attic. Middle of the sixth century B.C. Stoddard Collection. Yale University Art Gallery 1913.110.

The shoulder lekythos, a purely Attic vase type, was developed in the second quarter of the sixth century B.C. It rapidly came to dominate the earlier Deianeira type, characterized by an elongated oval body and lacking a distinct shoulder. The body of the lekythos exhibited here is broad below the shoulder and tapers toward the foot. The shape contrasts with the more cylindrical form that prevailed for lekythoi later in the century. The piece has an unusual flaring flat-topped mouth, unlike

31

31

the taller, narrower mouth typical of most black-figure shoulder lekythoi.

The neck is decorated with ascending black rays. Below the raised ring separating the neck from the shoulder is a band of little black tongues. On the shoulder, opposite the handle, is an upright black palmette with lateral lotus buds. It is flanked by a panther on the left and a lion on the right.

The scene on the body of the lekythos shows the combat between Herakles and Kyknos. Herakles wears the lion's skin, a short chiton, a sword and quiver at his side, and brandishes a club with the right hand. Kyknos wears a Doric helmet, a chiton, greaves, and a sword at his side, and defends himself with a large circular shield and a lance. Flanking the combatants are two observers on each side, carrying spears. The two nearest to Herakles and Kyknos are wearing striped himations over long chitons, while the outermost two are nude.

The exploits of Herakles, the most celebrated of antique heroes, were especially popular as subject matter for Attic black-figure vase paintings. The earliest literary version of the skirmish between Herakles and Kyknos is found in the 480-line poetic fragment, *The Shield of Herakles*, probably a sub-Hesiodic addition to the *Catalogue of Women*. According to the Hesiodic account, Kyknos had been robbing cattle brought for sacrifice to the precinct of Apollo. Enraged by this sacrilege, Apollo sought revenge through an armed encounter between Kyknos and the indomitable Herakles. Following an initial encounter in chariots, the combatants clashed on foot, and Herakles killed Kyknos with a spear. In later antique writers (e.g. Apollodoros, *Bibliotheke*), two separate figures named Kyknos appeared, one the son of Ares and Pyrene, the other son of Ares and Pelopia. However, the distinction between the two Kyknos characters is not clear-cut nor does it seem particularly relevant to the depictions of the combat with Herakles as they appear on black-figure vases.

While some representatives in Attic vase painting of the encounter between Herakles and Kyknos include other characters that are prominent in the Hesiodic account (e.g., see the oinochoe in Berlin, potted by Kolchos and painted by Lydos, Beazley, *ABV* 110, 37; as well as Herakles and Kyknos, Athena, Zeus, and Ares are identifiable), it was also very common to show the scene as an isolated man-to-man combat. On this lekythos, the figures flanking the central group of Herakles and Kyknos

should not be interpreted as identifiable participants in the action. Rather, they are anonymous onlookers, examples of a pictorial device very common in sixth century vase painting.

Dimension: H. 31.2 cm.

Description: Red: stripes of himations, manes of animals, beard, fillets, dots on shield, part of Herakles' chiton, ring dividing area of figural scene from lower part of body, other details in figural scene. White: decoration of shield, dots on himations, other details in figural scene.

Condition: Intact. Surface sheen dulled by action of chlorides. Added white decoration on shield turned whiter than the greenish-yellow of undamaged areas. Chipped near handle.

Bibliography: Sambon-Canessa Sale Catalogue, Paris, May, 1910, no. 143, plate XVII; Jay Hambidge, *Dynamic Symmetry: The Greek Vase* (New Haven 1920) 124–125, fig. 3; Rhys Carpenter, "Dynamic Symmetry: A Criticism," *AJA* 25 (1921) 32 ff., fig. 7; Baur, *Stoddard Catalogue* 74–76; Haspels, *ABL* 21.

J. N. B.

32. Little Black-Neck Lekythos

Attic. Mid-sixth century B.C. *Stoddard Collection. Yale University Art Gallery 1913.109.*

The scene represents two mounted horsemen. The right rider is a nude youth, the one on the left, a youth clothed in the chlamys frequently worn by cavalrymen. Both figures are unarmed and lack sufficient attributes to permit specific identification. However, the motif of riders and especially mounted hoplites is a common one on mid-sixth century black-figure vases. Its popularity perhaps reflects the frequent patronage of potters by Hippeis, a class whose members possessed adequate wealth to maintain a horse and hence participate in warfare.

The incision on the figures is rudimentary: the eyes of men and horses are simple circles, and the contours suggested by the black glaze are frequently ignored, as in the foot of the rider on the right.

The Little Black-neck Lekythoi are a sub-group of the Deianeira lekythos tradition which existed side by side with the more popular shoulder lekythos tradition. Of the various Deianeira shapes the Little Black-necks recall the type produced by the Pharos painter and his workshop. The Yale

32

in dilute glaze under the tongues and lines in the margins of the other three sides of the panel. One of these is the ground line, touched only by the left hind leg of each horse.

Condition: Severe flaking with exception of panel where slight. Mouth repaired, several chips missing. Two chips on foot. Black glaze lost on left foot of left horse and at several points on vertical lines framing panel. Red: horses manes except forelock of right horse.

Bibliography: Baur, *Stoddard Catalogue* 74, fig. 20; Haspels, *ABL* 195. On the subject see T. B. L. Webster, *Potter and Patron in Classical Athens* (London 1972), ch. 14.

C. O.

33. Black-Figure Amphora

Attic. Attributed to the Affecter. Ca. 540 B.C. Lent by Mr. and Mrs. Walter Bareiss. Bareiss no. 20.

The Affecter's style is one of the most easily recognized in all of Greek vase painting. The thick draped figures with tiny heads and the nudes with exaggerated angular joints on this amphora are unmistakably his. The curling thumbs and profuse added color are also characteristic. The Affecter and his stylistic cousin Elbows Out are the two primary artists of black-figure mannerist style.

The ovoid amphora that was the favored shape of the Affecter is a remnant of the Tyrrhenian Group of ten to twenty years earlier. His crowded scenes with many onlookers strung out around the vase and virtually no suggestion of depth also relate his style to the Tyrrhenian artists. Surely this is intentional. The Affecter's contemporaries Exekias and the Amasis Painter show concern for the interaction of their figures in space and a more elastic sense of body movement. The Affecter, on the other hand, is more of a pure formalist, preferring to explore patterns of the isolated figure in space. Extremities flying, his running or dancing figures suggest movement by the many directions in which their limbs extend. The sheer bulk of the bodies of his standing figures when played against their tiny heads creates a solidity difficult to achieve with normal proportions and more rounded contours.

The Affecter's mannered formalism far outweighs his interest in the mythological subjects that are his vehicles. It is often difficult to relate

vase shares the general characteristics of its class: the dull, uneven black glaze, the sprightly if careless figure decoration, and the two red lines which encircle the vase under the panel. It is the most globular of the extant Little Black-necks, and its shape is also unusual in the larger context of the Deianeira tradition.

Dimensions: H. 17.4 cm.

Description: A black glaze covers the entire vase except for the panel which, together with the tongue pattern above it, occupies two-thirds of one side of the lekythos. The scene is framed by a line

33, Side A

33, Side B

secondary figures in his scenes to the primary action. On this vase the combat between Theseus and the Minotaur is flanked by unidentifiable and unrelated figures.

The battle on the other side is watched by Apollo and three onlookers. Beazley identifies the subject as Herakles and Nessos; Apollo and the hind shown in small scale beneath his bow would be a reference to another of Herakles' quarrels. Herakles is shown without his omnipresent attribute, the lion skin, and it is tempting to suggest that he might instead be the Lapith King Perithoos battling the centaurs at his wedding, watched over by Apollo as on the sculptures of the West Pediment of the Temple of Zeus at Olympia. However, the Affecter's consistent use of the most common mythological subjects and conflation of unrelated scenes weighs against any certain interpretation.

Dimensions: H. 38.5 cm.

Description: Ovoid neck amphora with echinus mouth, torus foot, and round handles. Double rays on the foot. Above the scene, lotus buds, and framed alternating black and red tongues. On the neck, A and B, Komos. Profuse use of red for chitons, mantle details, beards, hair, etc. White: Minotaur's mouth and nose.

Condition: Broken and repaired, part of bird under handle missing. Black glaze worn on side A, especially figures 2, 3 and 4.

Bibliography: Basel, Münzen und Medaillen Auction 26 (5 October 1963) 46, no. 94; von Bothmer, *MMA Exh 2*, no. 16; Dietrich von Bothmer," Aspects of a Collection," *Metropolitan Museum of Art Bulletin* (June 1969) 430, fig. 5; Beazley, *Paralipomena* 111, no. 14 bis; Heidi Mommsen-Scharmer, *Der Affecter (Forschungen zur antiken Keramik Reihe 2: Kerameus)*, forthcoming.

S. M. B.

34

34. Black-Figure "Eye Cup"

Attic. Ca. 530–520 B.C. Yale University Art Gallery 1967.74.16.

Immediately striking are the two pairs of oversized, stylized eyes with great target-like irises which adorn the cup's exterior. Very probably apotropaic, it has been suggested that their illusionistic quality may also have come into play: when a reveler tipped his cup to drink, his companion would have seen the eyes and projected a face, that is, the handles would have become ears and the base a mouth.

Between each pair of eyes a Greek hoplite does battle with an Amazon, a member of the legendary tribe of fierce women warriors from the East. The two combat scenes conform to sixth century conventions. Costumes and weapons are standard. Men wear Corinthian helmets, women, high-crested Attic helmets with oblong cheek pieces; all wear short tunics, covering corselets, and greaves. The figures are armed with spears, swords in scabbards, and round shields (the *hoplon*). Greek shields are decorated with a pattern of circles within half-circles, Amazon shields with ivy. The nude youth with long red hair on side A who observes the struggle so impassively is a curious, though by no means unique, figure. Unrelated to the legend portrayed, he serves principally, it seems, to vary the composition. The Amazonomachy, so frequently depicted on Attic vases, appears rather seldom on exteriors of black-figured eye-cups; Dietrich von Bothmer lists only sixteen examples (*Amazons in Greek Art* [Oxford 1957] 235–50).

A fearsome *gorgoneion* in tondo form with large eyes, wide, toothful grin and extended tongue, curly hair and beard enlivens the interior of the

34, detail of interior

bowl. This apotropaic emblem, which represents the disembodied head of the Gorgon Medusa whom Perseus slew, is the most common interior decoration of eye cups.

Grapeless vines sprout from each handle, fill the area below it, and creep behind and underneath the eyes. Rays, solid black and outline in alternation, topped by two sets of triple lines, extend from the foot.

Exekias's masterful kylix in Munich (2044, Beazley, *ABV* 146, no. 21) a piece famous for its interior representation of Dionysos sailing, stands at the head of the series of Attic eye cups. This piece, like the Yale cup, is an early example of the Type A kylix, a type characterized by the presence of a fillet between foot and bowl. Hansjörg Bloesch's close analysis of cup form (*Formen Attischer Schalen von Exekias bis zum Ende des Strengen Stils* [Bern-Bümpliz 1940]) makes it possible to classify the Yale kylix further. Its spreading bowl which angles inward at the rim, short, concave foot and wide foot plate, and the smooth transition evident between its bowl and handle, connect it decisively with Bloesch's "Andokides-gruppe." Its slightly reduced proportions place it more specifically in the Circle of the Andokides group. Two features of the cup, its relatively flat fillet and simple, rounded handles, are more commonly associated with cups produced under the potter Nikosthenes. They may be taken as an indication of the degree of interchange between shops. Having been formally located, the eye cup may be dated to 530–20 B.C.

The painter, a noteworthy if not major master of the mature black-figure style, has yet to acquire an identity. It may be noted that an eye cup in Paris,

Louvre F 132 bis, with dueling Greeks on each side (*CVA*, Louvre no. 10, pls. 99, 100) and another in the Ricketts and Shannon collection in the Fitzwilliam Museum, Cambridge, with two representations of a warrior leading a horse (*CVA*, pls. 4, 8, 9), also unattributed, bear striking stylistic similarities to Yale's eye cup.

Dimensions: H. 11.6 cm.; D. 31 cm.

Description: Type A kylix: liberal use of incision and accents of red and white on exterior figures and interior tondo. Concentric circles of eyes incised with compass, colored from inside out, black, red, white, black. Interior of bowl painted black; circle around *gorgoneion* and strip at lip in reserve. Insides of handle reserved; misfiring evident on right handle. Foot black with reserved fillet and base. Inner wall of recess in foot black. On bottom: | | | : : is incised.

Condition: Reconstructed from fragments. Damage at breaks. Several hiatuses in bowl as restored. Handles and foot complete. White paint, applied over black, worn; extensive losses of white on side A.

Bibliography: Dietrich von Bothmer, *Amazons in Greek Art* (Oxford 1957) 71, pl. LI, 3.

E. S.

35. Black-Figure Lekythos

Attic. Workshop of the Edinburgh Painter. Ca. 500 B.C. Stoddard Collection. Yale University Art Gallery 1913.111.

Apollo, identifiable by the lyre case on his back, mounts a chariot drawn by four strange beasts. Hermes with his petasos, caduceus, and winged boots gestures to the woman facing him on his left. This woman wears a polos, a cylindrical headdress which distinguishes her from the younger woman with a red fillet in her hair. She stands at the head of the quadriga and motions to the beasts with her extremely long arms. The identity of these two women and the beasts raises an important iconographic question.

The scene has been described by most scholars as the Chariot of Admetos (Apollodoros, *Bibliotheke* I. ix. 14–15) largely because of its "weird chariot." Apollo was condemned by Zeus to servitude for one year under the rule of Admetos, King of Pherae. In order for Admetos to win his bride, Alcestis, he was commanded to yoke a boar and a lion to his chariot. The Yale vase supposedly illustrates Apollo yoking this chariot for Admetos, but the evidence is unconvincing. The Edinburgh Painter is noted for his clear and unambiguous mythical depictions (Haspels, *ABL*, 88). If he wished Admetos' tale to be told he would certainly present the characters in a distinguishable manner. Yet Admetos and Alcestis are missing on the Yale vase, and the biga of the myth is here presented as a quadriga of two lions and two boars. Some have identified these finely executed beasts as a lion, panther, boar, and wolf, but the traces of fugitive white used to paint the last animal's tusks associate it clearly with a boar. Furthermore, the second animal, who looks up and out at us, belongs to the tradition of the Corinthian panther but has been modified by the addition of a curly mane, connecting it more closely with the lion family than with the sleek panther group.

Three contemporary vases depict similar "weird chariots" and clearly do not present the chariot of Admetos. They are a neck amphora by the Diosphos painter (Louvre CA. 1961) with Cadmus and Harmonia in a biga of a lion and a boar, accompanied by Apollo and identified by inscriptions; an oinochoe from Göttingen which presents a marriage couple in a troika drawn by a boar, a lion, and a wolf accompanied by Hermes and Apollo; and a oinochoe from Leningrad (Hermitage #28) showing a young maiden, probably Artemis, mounting a chariot drawn by two boars, a lion and a wolf (see Konrad Schauenburg, "Zu Darstellungen aus der Sage der Admet und der Kadmos," *Gymnasium* 64 [1957] pl. 1, 2, fig. p. 212).

The figures on the Yale vase represent a standard grouping of Apollo, his sister Artemis, their mother Leto, and the ever present deity of journey, Hermes. An amphora by the Rycroft Painter (Oxford, Ashmolean Museum 1965.118, John Boardman, *Athenian Black-figure Vases* [London 1974] fig. 226) represents Leto with polos mounting her chariot drawn by horses. Standing to her left is her son Apollo, followed by Hermes and Artemis, who stands before the chariot aiding her mother in calming the beasts, as she does her brother on the Yale vase. This vase illustrates an earlier rendering of the group, more finely executed and less exotic in taste. The composition of the Yale vase was most likely based on such a model, rather than on representations of the Admetos tale. Most of the indisputable representations of the Admetos story are, like the preserved literary accounts of it, several centuries later than our vase. Perhaps the deities represented here are about to

leave for one of the select mortal weddings like that of Peleus and Thetis or Cadmus and Harmonia or are even preparing the chariot for Admetos, but these speculations go beyond what is visible in the painter's representation.

Dimensions: H. 32.1 cm.

Description: Brown clay, lustrous black glaze, red ground with incised details. Tapered cylindrical form characteristic of the Edinburgh Painter, with cup-shaped mouth and thick reserved torus foot. Below the scene, three red lines encircle the vase; above the scene, a double row of dots, forming triangles, bordered by lines; on the shoulder, the characteristic seven black palmettes with tendrils, three grouped in the center, two on either side.

Condition: Excellent except for loss of the fugitive white paint, used for female flesh, some traces of which can be seen overlapping the black base.

Provenance: From Tarentum.

Bibliography: Paul Hartwig, *Ausonia 7* (Rome 1912) 107s; Baur, *Stoddard Catalague no. 111*, fig. 19; Haspels, *ABL* 86s, 216s, 221 no. 1; Buitron, *NEC* 52, no. 21; John Boardman, *Athenian Black Figure Vases* (London 1974) 147, fig. 240; Dietrich von Bothmer, rev. of Boardman, *Athenian Black Figure Vases*, Art Bulletin 57 (1975); for the artist see also: Beazley, *ABV* 476–480.

C. K.

36. Black-Figure Lekythos

Attic. Early work by the Athena Painter. Ca. 500 B.C. Stoddard Collection. Yale University Art Gallery 1913.112.

The Athena Painter, named for his favorite subject, was one of several late black-figure artists who specialized in the production of small vessels, such as lekythoi, skyphoi, and oinochoai. Primarily a lekythos painter, he adopted the tall, cylindrical shaped shoulder lekythos popularized slightly earlier by the Edinburgh Painter, eventually introducing minor decorative changes to the type. His earliest lekythoi, of which the Yale vase is an example, are red ground. He later switched to the white ground technique and painted the necks black. His work is generally of good quality. The subjects on his vases are usually drawn from mythology, with Athena and Herakles being his favorites. The drawing style of the Yale vase closely resembles that of other vases by the Athena

35

35

Painter in facial and anatomical details.

The subject of this painting is Poseidon on a winged hippocamp. The hippocamp faces right while Poseidon, holding a trident, looks back to the left. Two dolphins swim downward to the rear.

Poseidon was a brother of Zeus, and at one time considered a general water deity. He later supplanted a group of more ancient sea divinities, such as Nereus and Amphitrite, to become the Greeks' main god of the ocean. It is as ruler of the seas, astride a mythological steed combining aspects of horse, bird, and fish that he appears on this lekythos.

Poseidon's close relationship to the hippocamp may stem from his earlier ties with horses, symbolized by one of his titles, Poseidon Hippios. In the Peloponnesus in particular he was regarded as the god of horses and earthquakes. He appears as an equestrian early in the sixth century on several Corinthian pinax fragments. The oldest preserved example of Poseidon on a hippocamp is found on a Middle Corinthian alabastron, but it is not until the second half of the sixth century that the theme becomes common on Attic pottery, reaching its fullest development in the various examples by the Athena Painter.

Poseidon was recognized as the guardian of the city Tarentum, from which this lekythos is reputed to have come. While it is not known whether the Athena Painter had prior knowledge of this vase's destination, it is known that when it was painted (ca. 500 B.C.) the red-figure style was dominant and popular, and much black-figure work was being exported to the more artistically conservative colonies. This may account for a black-figure lekythos depicting Poseidon ultimately finding its way to the southern Italian colony Tarentum.

Dimensions: H. 25.4 cm.

Description: Reddish fabric painted with lustrous black glaze on base, mouth, and exterior of handle. Top of mouth, neck, greater part of shoulder and body, inside of handle, and edge of foot are reserved. Ring of black tongues on neck. Five black palmettes on shoulder with middle palmette inverted. Band at shoulder of dotted zig-zag framed by red stripes. Bottom of figural panel bordered by two red bands. Bridle, harness, mane, facial stripe, dorsal and pectoral fins, and dots on wings of hippocamp are red. Belly of hippocamp white. Red ring at tip of tail. Wreath and beard of Poseidon red. Chiton dotted white.

Condition: Broken and mended. Figural design intact. All restoration visible.

36

36

36

Provenance: Said to come from Tarentum.

Bibliography: Baur, *Stoddard Catalogue* 77–8, pl. 6; Haspels, *ABL* 255, no. 26. On the artist see: Haspels *ABL* 141–165 and 254–260; Beazley *ABV* 522–524. For the subject see: L.R. Farnell, *The Cults of the Greek States* IV (Oxford 1907); Ursula Heimberg, *Das Bild des Poseidon in der Griechischen Vasenmalerei* (Freiburg 1968).

J. K.

37. White-Ground Lekythos

Attic. Attributed to the Beldam Painter. Ca. 470–460 B.C. The Hobart and Edward Small Moore Memorial Collection. Yale University Art Gallery 1955.4.103.

A groom is shown unharnessing a four-horse chariot. Both the representation of an unharnessing scene and the view of an empty chariot are rare in Greek vase painting. The Beldam painter portrays groom and horses in relaxed poses. The groom has unharnessed the trace-horses, already tethered to the car, and the near pole-horse, which has backed away from the car and turned to stare outward. He is engaged in unfastening the reins from the other pole-horse. The unhurried movement of the figures evokes a sense of calm disorder and reverie which contrasts markedly with the aura of tense anticipation and bustling activity of traditional harnessing scenes. Here, the homely quality of the unusual scene, coupled with the emptiness of the chariot, further define the funerary character of the lekythos.

The most striking feature of the scene is the knock-kneed near pole-horse, whose contorted form constitutes a bold attempt at foreshortening. Throughout the first half of the fifth century red-figure vase painters experimented with three-quarter views, foreshortening, and perspectival renderings. The Beldam painter shares this interest, although in other respects his lekythos reflects the pictorial style characteristic of the outmoded black-figure technique.

The picture field extends down to the curve at the base and the figures stand on a well-defined ground line. Below the field are a zig-zag band and a series of incised lines; above is a rightward key between pairs of black lines and on the shoulder rays and tongues. The Beldam Painter used fine, close incisions to articulate the horses' manes, eyes, and tails and compact, curving lines hooked at the ends for the folds of the groom's chiton and the curling ends of his hair.

The lekythos contains an inner receptacle for perfumed oil; that is, a small cup attached to the neck extends inside the hollow body of the vase. The vessel thus appears to have a large capacity but can hold only a few ounces of oil. The Beldam potter is credited with the invention—as early as 475 B.C.—of such false-bottomed lekythoi, economically designed for funerary use. A vent-hole is provided, through the handle and shoulder at their junction, to allow gases to escape from the sealed lower chamber during firing. The shape of the lekythos is also innovative. The body is tall and tapering; just below the shoulder the cylinder flares inward at a sharp angle.

During the second quarter of the fifth century the white-ground technique was confined largely to funerary vases, particularly the lekythos. The Beldam Painter, whose career lasted from about 480 to 450 B.C., was a specialist in the decoration of lekythoi and the use of the white-ground; he was the last significant black-figure vase painter in Athens. This lekythos belongs to the early and best phase of his career.

Dimensions: H. 30.3 cm.; D. 9.8 cm.

Description: False bottomed lekythos, air hole at handle base. Below the scene reserved bands and a band of net pattern. Above, a rightward key between pairs of black lines. On the shoulder, which is red-ground, rays below black vertical lines.

Condition: Broken and repaired; small losses restored, including an area of the chest and left arm of the groom. Slight salt damage in the field. Glaze oxidized red in many areas.

Provenance: Formerly in the Polytechneion, Athens; presented by the Greek Government to Mrs. William Moore in 1932.

Bibliography: P. B. Hartwig, *Die Griechischen Meisterschalen,* (Stuttgart 1893) 110; Walter Wrede, "Kriegers Ausfahrt," *AthMitt* 41 (1916) 234, 353–4, no. 174; Ernst Pfuhl, *Malerei und Zeichnung der Griechen* (Munich 1923) I, 294, III, fig. 279; Haspels, *ABL* 177, 190, 226, no. 10; L. D. Caskey and J. D. Beazley, *Attic Vase Paintings in the Museum of Fine Arts, Boston* II (Oxford 1931–63) 22; Bernard Andreae, "Herakles und Alkyoneus," *JdI* 77 (1962) 158–9, n. 77; Beazley, *Paralipomena* 292.

W. T. O.

37

37

37

38. Black-Figure Amphora

*Attic. Attributed to the Rycroft Painter. Ca. 510
B.C. Lent by Mr. and Mrs. Walter Bareiss. Bareiss
no. 3.*

A chariot wheeling round is seen on side A. The
quadriga is driven by a youth in a white tunic,
accompanied by a hoplite whose white-edged
shield appears to protect both himself and his
driver. In a conventional formula for three-quarter
views, the two outer horses are seen in profile
while the two inner horses turn towards the
viewer, their muzzles overlapping. This view of the
quadriga seems to originate with Group E, ca.
560–545 B.C.; as an exercise in perspective drawing
it continued to interest artists to the end of the
black-figure period. The subject frequently occurs
as part of a fight scene, commonly on the shoulders
of hydriae. Few representations are demonstrably
mythical, and only three, including two prize Pan-
athenaics (Beazley, *ABV* 369, 112–113), are definitely part of a chariot race. The majority,
including the Bareiss amphora, show an uniden-
tified hoplite and charioteer in a scene with no
mythological or narrative context. At most a general reference to the heroic past may be understood from the representation of a form of warfare
no longer used.

Dionysos riding on a donkey appears on side B,
accompanied by two satyrs. Dionysos, dressed in
a mantle and a short white tunic, holds a drinking
horn. The subject is generally limited to black-
figure. The god of wine surrounded by a varying
assortment of satyrs and maenads appears frequently as a secondary subject on black-figure

38, Side A

38, Side B

vases. No specific ritual is described by these scenes, nor is any relation to the primary subject of the vase usually intended. Such standard Dionysiac subjects were favored by the Rycroft Painter.

The Rycroft Painter is related to Psiax and the Priam Painter. All three were active after the introduction of red-figure and show the influence of the increased fluidity of·form and movement permitted by the new technique.

The Bareiss amphora and four other type B amphorae form a group of closely related wheeling chariot scenes (Paris, Cabinet des Médailles 208 [Beazley, *ABV* 336, 13]; Laon 37977 [Beazley, *ABV* 336, 14 and *CVA* pl. 4,4 and pl. 6]; Montecito, Brundage Collection, destroyed by fire in 1964 [Beazley, *Paralipomena* 149]; Rhodes 13447 from Tomb 247 in Cameirus [Beazley, *ABV* 336, 15]). The Bareiss, Brundage, and Laon amphorae have Dionysos on a donkey on Side B, and the Paris amphora shows Dionysos and maenads. Each chariot is driven by a charioteer accompanied by a hoplite; the Brundage, Paris, and Rhodes vases add an archer to the right, the Laon chariot is framed by archers. Beazley calls the Laon, Paris, and Rhodes amphorae late works by the Rycroft Painter; the Bareiss and Brundage amphorae must be late as well. The Laon amphora is probably the earliest of the five. Its incision is the most careful and the taller proportions of its figures closer to the painter's early work and that of Psiax.

Dimensions: H. 38.1 cm.

Description: Type B amphora. Lotus buds and intersecting arcs with dots border the top of the panels. Rays above the foot. Red bands: 1 above and 2 below the panels, 1 above and 1 below the reserved band with rays, 2 on the mouth, at the inner and outer edges. Red: side A: charioteer's fillet, stripe at the base of the horses' manes, chest harness of horses 1 and 3 (solid), dots on chest harnesses of horses 2 and 4; side B: all three beards, alternate leaves of Dionysos' ivy wreath. White: side A: charioteer's tunic, shield border, dots on helmet crest, stars on the two inner horses, teeth of outer horses, dots on reins and bridles and below chest harnesses; side B: short tunic worn by Dionysos, spots on his mantle, muzzle, and stripe on chest, belly, and rump of the donkey.

Condition: Intact. Circular dent (misfired) on Side A. Added color well preserved.

Bibliography: Beazley, *Paralipomena* 149, no. 15 bis.

s. m. b.

39 & 40. Panathenaic Amphorae

Attic. Attributed to the Kleophrades Painter. Ca. 500–480 B.C. Gift of Frederic W. Stevens, B.A. 1858. Yale University Art Gallery 1909.12 and 1909.13.

Panathenaic Amphorae, filled with olive oil, were given as prizes to victorious athletes at the Panhellenic games held once every four years from the middle of the sixth century to the end of the Hellenistic period. They were commissioned by the state during the years between the Panathenaic festivals; as many as a thousand were commissioned for each series of games.

The shape, decorative format, and black-figure technique used for the prize vases were canonical by around 530 B.C. The obverse depicted Athena, the patron goddess of Athens, in a war-like pose with helmet, spear, and shield, and flanked by columns with cocks. The inscription "a prize from the games at Athens" usually appeared on this side near the left column. The reverse side showed the particular sporting event for which the amphora was awarded: a chariot race, as here, a horse race, wrestling match, foot race, and so forth.

As highly valued prizes, Panathenaic Amphorae were decorated by only the best artists: Lydos and Exekias among the black-figure artists, the Berlin Painter, the Kleophrades Painter, and the Achilles Painter among red-figure painters. The use of black-figure technique did not preclude the influence of red-figure style as artists became more adept at anatomy and at the illusion of three-dimensional space. Thus, although Panathenaic Amphorae were supposed to remain traditional and "archaic" during the fifth century and afterwards, they do not, becoming instead a mannered mixture of old and new.

Nine Panathenaic Amphorae, including these two, have been attributed to the Kleophrades Painter. Beazley has suggested that they all belong to the early part of the artist's career, ca. 500–480 B.C. Stylistically the thick-set figures, large heads, and relaxed body poses resemble the style of his teacher, Euthymides, whose work the Kleophrades Painter closely imitated during his early period. The Pegasus shield device, asterisk chiton motifs, long arms, strong lips and chins, prominent nose curls, thick necks, and large ears are characteristic of the Kleophrades Painter and unmistakably identify him as the painter of these two vessels. Another Panathenaic with a chariot scene on the reverse in New York is very close to

39, Side A

39, Side B

these (Metropolitan Museum of Art 07.286.79, Beazley, *ABV* 404, no. 6); the entire group is consistent in style and detail.

(39.)

Dimensions: H. 65.2 cm., as restored.

Description: Red: on side A, rim of shield, edge of helmet, border of peplos, combs, gullets, and breasts of cocks. Side B: charioteer's beard, part of the chariot, horses' tails. On both sides: line circling vase at bases of panels. White: Side A:

Athena's flesh, Pegasus; Side B: charioteer's chiton.

Condition: Broken and repaired; overpainting removed; missing pieces restored in plaster and clay, painted orange.

Bibliography: J. D. Beazley, *The Development of Attic Black-figure* (Berkeley 1951) 111, n. 37; Beazley, *ABV* 404, no. 4; Buitron, *NEC* 25–26; J. D. Beazley, *The Kleophrades Painter* (Mainz 1974) 21, no. 97 bis.

40, Side A

40, Side B

(40.)

Dimensions: H. 65.5 cm. as restored.

Description: Red: Side A: dots on rim of shield, Athena's fillet and belt fringe and hem border of chiton, upper wings and combs of cocks, tongues, base line. Side B: charioteer's beard, horses' tails, manes, chest harness, base line, tongues. White: Side A: Athena's flesh and Pegasus. Side B: charioteer's chiton.

Condition: Broken and repaired, with restorations of plaster and clay. Original surface heavily overpainted, now cleaned. Remaining restorations painted.

Bibliography: Beazley, *ABV* 404, no. 5; J. D. Beazley, *The Kleophrades Painter* (Mainz 1974) 21, no. 97 ter.

D. T.

RED-FIGURE VASES

41. Bilingual Kylix

Attic. Attributed to Oltos. Ca. 520–510 B.C. Lent by Mr. and Mrs. Walter Bareiss. Bareiss no. 81.

Bilingual vases, cups or pots decorated in both black-figure and red-figure, are frequently found in early red-figure vase painting. Most of these occur in the work of the first generation of red-figure vase painters (ca. 530–510 B.C.) and become very rare after the beginning of the fifth century, even though some black-figure ware continues to be produced. As is commonly the case with bilingual kylikes, the interior of the vase is in black-figure and the exterior is in red-figure.

On the interior of the cup, the tondo is filled with a running figure, probably a reveler, around who is inscribed MEMNON KAΛO[Σ] meaning "Memnon is handsome." In keeping with the conventions of black-figure technique, red is added to the hair and beard of the runner, as well as to the himation draped over his left shoulder and tucked across his right arm.

The exterior is decorated with a single figure placed between a pair of apotropaic eyes and two large palmettes connected by a stem to the handles of the cup. The figure of the youth is unclothed.

41, detail of interior

This cup is typical of the eye-cups painted by Oltos, one of the earliest red-figure masters of cup painting. The pattern on the exterior of a palmette with closed leaves on either side of the large eyes occurs in a number of his cups, and there is little variation in the treatment of the ornamental forms from cup to cup. The eyes on this kylix have a red pupil, a reserved ring, and a reserved margin around the eye itself. (For the significance of the apotropaic eyes, see cat. no. 34).

As is often the case with bilingual eye-cups by Oltos, the black-figure is technically better than the red-figure, which suggests that the artist was perhaps trained in black-figure. There are virtually no details added to the body of the nude youth on the exterior, while the artist has incised many anatomical details on the black-figure reveler in the tondo.

Oltos is known through two signed vases, one in Berlin and one in Tarquinia. Beazley has attributed almost one hundred other vases to him, most of which are cups. These reveal a number of distinctive characteristics. The figures tend to be short and stocky, with a minimum of interior articulation of the body, especially in red-figure. The noses are usually long and pointed, and the eye is often narrow and oblique. The reveler on the interior is in a posture frequently found in the cups of Oltos: the legs are in a exaggerated running pose, one arm is bent at the elbow, and the other is stretched forward. The head looks back, suggesting that the figure is pursued. Oltos often draws hands with long elegant fingers, as can be seen in the tondo of this kylix, where the hand of the reveler droops affectedly against the edge of the circle. Another characteristic of his style are the long, flat feet visible on both the interior and exterior figures of this vase.

The inscription to Memnon on the interior of this cup appears in a number of vases by Oltos. It appears most frequently in vases attributed to the first half of the artist's career. Use of the bilingual technique also seems to occur in the early period of his style, thus suggesting a date for this kylix of 520 B.C. Although all of Oltos' eye-kylikes are very similar, this one is particularly close to an eye-kylix in the Altenburg Museum (no. 224; Beazley, *ARV²* 44).

Dimensions: D. of bowl 32.6 cm.

Description: Black line within reserved band around tondo. Reserved band encircles vase on exterior beneath scene. Red: youth's hair (interior), pupils of eyes.

41

41

Inscriptions: In the field in the tondo: MEM-NON KAΛO[Σ]

Condition: Broken and repaired. Restoration on the face, arms, leg, and drapery of the interior figure.

Bibliography: von Bothmer, *MMA Exh 6*, no. 70; Dietrich von Bothmer, "Aspects of a Collection," *Metropolitan Museum of Art Bulletin* (June 1969) 431, figs. 6 and 7. General: Beazley, *ARV²* 34–43; Ada Bruhn, *Oltos and Early Red-Figure Vase Painting* (Copenhagen 1943); F. P. Johnson, "Oltos and Euphronios," *Art Bulletin* 19 (1937) 537–560.

C. B.

42. Red-Figure Kylix

Attic. Near the Gales Painter. Ca. 510–500 B.C. Stoddard Collection. Yale University Art Gallery 1913.163.

The tondo shows a symposion scene, with the reclining nude figures of a youth and a flute-girl locked in an amorous embrace. The platform on which the figures rest is an abbreviated suggestion of a couch, a pictorial device commonly used within the limited space of kylix tondos, especially in early red-figure painting. The striped pillow against which the youth leans and the basket which hangs to the left of the reclining couple are among the furnishings and objects of domestic use seen most often in painted symposia. Although not without precedent in Corinthian and Attic black-figure painting, this type of symposion scene enjoyed its greatest popularity during the period of early red-figure painting, when the activities of daily life became increasingly important as subject matter in Greek art. Properly speaking, the symposion was a drinking party that began only after dining was finished. Not surprisingly, the kylix was the favored vessel for decoration with scenes of symposia. Such subject matter was also considered appropriate for kraters. The double flute held by the girl in the scene on the Yale cup identifies her as a performer who provided entertainment at drinking parties; the scene suggests equally the non-musical activities of such evenings.

The execution of this scene exemplifies the experimentation that was going on among the pioneer red-figure painters in an attempt to develop new methods of suggesting the three-dimensionality of the human form. The convention of piecing together a figure with some parts of the body seen in profile view and others shown frontally was taken over by early red-figure artists from black-figure painting, but the combination of one profile and one frontal leg in a single figure, used in drawing the youth on this cup, was an innovation of the red-figure pioneers. The painter of the Yale kylix did not resolve successfully all the problems presented by this pose, and it is difficult to imagine exactly where each of the youth's legs connects with his torso. The heads of both the youth and the flute-girl are shown in profile view, following the general practice of early red-figure painting. Though the eyes are shown in front view, the pupils are placed nearer the inner corners, a first step toward the more naturalistic rendering of the eye in profile that reached its full development with the free style.

J.D. Beazley has hesitantly attributed the decoration of this cup to the Gales Painter, an artist in Beazley's Pioneer Group who painted two lekythoi signed by the potter Gales (from Gela, Sicily: now Boston 13.195 and Syracuse 26967; see Beazley, ARV^2 35–36). The Boston lekythos shows a procession scene with cows being led to sacrifice and the Syracuse lekythos a *komos* with the poet Anakreon flanked by two youths. An examination of the piece in Boston, which is by far the better preserved of the two lekythoi, indicates many significant differences between the working method and style of its painter and the painter of the Yale kylix. Preliminary sketch lines were used much more extensively on the Yale kylix than on the Boston lekythos. Moreover, while dilute glaze was used on the lekythos to indicate many secondary anatomical details, it is lacking from the kylix. There are also notable differences in the manner of rendering a number of anatomical parts, including chins, noses, ears, eyes, and hair. On the other hand, there are important similarities in the rendering of mouths, eyebrows, male torsos, and hands.

When the evidence of these stylistic comparisons is weighed in the balance, it seems that the drawing on the Yale cup differs significantly enough from that on the two signed lekythoi, that an attribution of the cup to the Gales Painter is not warranted. Perhaps, if there were more extant pieces securely attributed to the Gales Painter, the range of variation within the body of work would appear broader, and a piece as different from the Boston and Syracuse lekythoi as the Yale kylix might be admitted to the oeuvre. However, given only the two lekythoi as secure points of reference, it seems best to conclude that the artist of the Yale cup is "near the Gales Painter" but is not to be identified with him.

Dimensions: H. 9.2 cm.; diam. of bowl 22.3 cm.

Description: Type B kylix. Foot in two degrees. Solid stem. Exterior undecorated. Tondo defined by two reserved circles. Extensive preliminary sketch. In many places painting does not follow sketch lines. Traces of red: wreaths, basket, strings, inscription. Parts of exterior and foot misfired.

Inscriptions: ΗΟ ΠΑΙΣ [Κ]ΑΛΟΣ

Condition: Broken and repaired. Left handle and part of adjacent rim restored in plaster. In-painting with flat black. Minor loss to right knee of youth; otherwise, figural scene intact.

Bibliography: Jay Hambidge, *Dynamic Sym-*

42

metry: *The Greek Vase* (New Haven 1920) 122, fig. 12; Baur, *Stoddard Catalogue* 108; Hans Licht, *Sittengeschichte Griechenlands* II (Dresden and Zurich, 1925–1928) 47; L.D. Caskey and J.D. Beazley, *Attic Vase Paintings in the Museum of Fine Arts, Boston*, Part I (London 1931) 10–11.

J. N. B.

43. Red-Figure Plate

Attic. Attributed to Paseas. Ca. 520–510 B.C. Stoddard Collection. Yale University Art Gallery 1913.169.

The abduction of Cassandra is drawn from the story of the Sack of Troy probably as recounted in two lost early Greek epics, the *Iliupersis* by Arc-tinus of Miletus and the *Little Iliad* by Lesches of Mytilene, both writing in the second half of the eighth century B.C. (M. I. Wiencke "An Epic Theme in Greek Art," *AJA* 58 [1954] 285–291). Cassandra is shown nude, clutching the drapery of the statue of Athena from which Ajax, the son of Oileus, grasping her arms, is attempting to drag her. This prophetess, whose credibility was taken from her by Apollo after she tricked him out of promised favors, was raped by Ajax and taken back to Greece as a prize by Agamemnon, only to be mur-dered there by his wife, Clytemnestra. Cas-sandra, the daughter of the Trojan King Priam, warned the Trojans of the danger of the Trojan Horse and foretold the fall of the city, but her warnings went unheeded. The abduction scene occurs both isolated, as here, and as part of a larger cycle of scenes from the Fall of Troy,

43

usually including the death of Priam and Astyanax (e.g. a hydria by the Kleophrades Painter, Naples 2422 [Beazley, *ARV*² 189, no. 74]).

Most black-figure representations show Athena striding forward. As the red-figure style developed, Athena became more obviously a sculpture. Both feet were shown together and flat, sometimes on a base. Frequently she is on a smaller scale than the rest of the figures, or, as in the Naples hydria, wears the old Doric peplos while the Trojan women wear the more modern chiton. The use of the smaller scale for Cassandra, however, is a tradition retained from black-figure representations, as is the Corinthian helmet worn by Ajax.

Paseas, whose name is known from a signed black-figure plaque found on the Acropolis in Athens (John Boardman, "A Name for the Cerberus Painter?" *JHS* 75 [1955] 154), was among the early red-figure artists. His nearest stylistic kin is Psiax, who also worked in both techniques. The close relation of this plate to the black-figure style,

particularly to the meticulously detailed style of Psiax, suggests that it is an early work. Compared to the experimental drawings of his contemporaries, Euphronios and Euthymides, Paseas' early works are conservative. He seems to show no interest in the back views and twisted poses but is content to work within the stiff, frontal poses inherited from black-figure. His later works, however, (a red-figure plate in Boston, Museum of Fine Arts 03.785 [Beazley, *ARV*² 163,1] showing two athletes is characteristic) show a simplification of form and an interest in foreshortening that may reflect the influence of Oltos.

Dimensions: H. 2.7 cm.; D. 18.7 cm.

Description: The figures stand on a thin reserved line. A reserved band marks the transition from the bottom to the wall of the plate, another at the edge. Crest of Athena's helmet cropped so as not to violate the border. Red: Ajax's baldric. No traces of aegis on Athena's chiton.

Inscriptions: ΑΙΑΣ behind Ajax; ΚΑΤΑΔΡΑ be-

44

low the ground line;AΘENAIA behind the statue.

Condition: Broken and repaired, with missing pieces restored and painted.

Bibliography: Beazley, VA 13–14, fig. 5; J. C. Hoppin, *A Handbook of Attic Red-Figured Vases* I (Cambridge, Mass. 1919) 144, no. 4; Baur, *Stoddard Catalogue* 111–112, pl. 15; Ernst Pfuhl, *Malerei und Zeichnung der Griechen* (Munich 1923) 433 (identified as the Io Painter); Juliette Davreux, *La Légende de la Prophétesse Cassandre* (Liège 1942) fig. 45; Beazley, *ARV*² 163–4 no. 3; Buitron, *NEC* 70.

S. M. B.

44. Red-Figure Plate.

Attic. Attributed to Paseas. Ca. 520–510 B.C. Stoddard Collection. Yale University Art Gallery 1913.170.

Dionysos, holding a kantharos and an ivy branch, faces left. A satyr dances in front of the god, his right elbow bent, his left hand held to his forehead, his left knee held high, and the toes of his right foot just visible on the reserved line on which both figures stand. This minimal treatment of a scene usually filled with cavorting satyrs and maenads is typical of plate decoration of this period. Psiax, to whom our artist is closely related in time and style, favored single figures in his five surviving plates (e.g. London, British Museum B 590 [Beazley, *ABV* 294,19]); see also H. R. W. Smith, "New Aspects of the Menon Painter," *University of California Publications in Archaeology* 1 [1959] 59).

John Boardman suggests that Paseas was basically a red-figure artist who used the older black-figure technique on the eight white ground plaques from the Acropolis that are his only black-figure works (John Boardman, *Athenian Black Figure Vases* [London 1974] 106). All the plaques show Athena striding forward in much the same way that she appears on Panathenaic amphorae. Perhaps the unusual inscription on the one signed plaque "one of the paintings of Paseas" bears some relation to the standard prize inscription of the Panathenaic amphorae, but whether it is ironic, disappointed, as Boardman suggests, or unintentional is not clear.

Five of the nine plates attributed by Beazley to Paseas, including this one, were found in Chiusi; no provenance is known for the other four. A tenth plate by the artist, close in style to the Boston plate with Athletes (03.785, Beazley, *ARV²* 163,1), also has no provenance (Basel, Münzen und Medaillen Auction no. 22, [May 13, 1961] 83, no. 157). A kylix fragment from Populonia and a standlet from Vulci join this group in suggesting that aside from the Acropolis plaques, which probably were a special commission, the major market for the works of Paseas may have been in Italy.

Dimensions: H. 2.4 cm.; D. 18.7 cm.

Description: Two reserved bands around the scene, another at the rim. Ring base pierced for suspension. Red: leaves of the ivy branch.

Condition: Broken and repaired with missing pieces restored and painted.

Provenance: From Chiusi.

Bibliography: Beazley, *VA* 13–14; J.C. Hoppin, *A Handbook of Attic Red-Figured Vases I* (Cambridge, Mass. 1919) 144, no. 4; Baur, *Stoddard Catalogue* 112, pl. 15; Beazley, *ARV²* 163–4, no. 4; Buitron, *NEC* 71.

S. M. B.

45, Side A

45. Red-Figure Nolan Amphora

Attic. Attributed to the Berlin Painter. Ca. 490 B.C. Lent by Mr. and Mrs. Walter Bareiss, Bareiss no. 15.

The vigorous line and the energetic poses of the figures on this amphora are typical of the early work of the Berlin Painter. As is usually the case with his vases, each side is decorated with a single figure standing on an ornamental border. The earlier convention of enclosing the figure within a decorative frame has disappeared, and the figures are now designed to harmonize with the profile of the vase rather than an enclosed rectangular space.

The figure on side B is an enigma and seems unique in the Berlin Painter's vases. He has been described as an old man (Beazley), and there are various representations of old men in vase paint-

ing which are in some respects similar to this figure. Two examples occur on a hydria in Naples by the Kleophrades painter which depicts the Sack of Troy (Museo Nazionale 2422, Beazley, *ARV²* 189). On this vase Anchises and Priam are shown with stippled beards and white hair, quite similar to that of the figure on side B of the Bareiss amphora. However, the facial features, particularly the nose and lips and the woolly hair which is the same color as the face give this figure a look that is distinct from representations of old men, and suggest that instead he may be Black. Blacks do occur in Greek vase painting as early as the sixth century, often in illustrations of the myth of the Egyptian King Busiris. One well-known example is a pelike by the Pan Painter with this scene in the National Museum in Athens (9683, Beazley, *ARV²* 554) where the facial features and treatment of the hair

45, Side B

hind him as though to balance his forward movement. The other has one hand on his hip and one hand flung forward. The himation of the younger dancer is thrown over his left arm, while that of the other dancer covers his shoulder and swings in front of his body.

The revelers seem to be engaged in the type of spontaneous after-dinner dance which sometimes took place after large and extended banquets. Dances of this type are often depicted on vases, frequently with nude or semi-nude figures carrying wine-cups or jars. The Greeks seem to have believed that there was an element of divine inspiration in dancing (Plato, *Laws* 653D-E) and this belief, when combined with the quantities of wine consumed at these feasts, may account for the elevated expressions of the revelers.

The internal anatomical details are added in dilute glaze, as are the dots on the hair and beard of the Black dancer. Red is used for the wreaths in the dancers' hair. The beautifully flowing line, precision of the drawing, and elegant simplicity of the figures are characteristic of the Berlin Painter. The himatia are rendered in naturalistic folds, and their swing is essential to the sense of movement.

The heart-shaped ornament in this vase is unusual, and appears only in one other vase attributed to the Berlin Painter: a Nolan Amphora in Capua which is also considered to be an early work (No. 217, *CVA* II, plate 4, figs. 1, 3, 4, 6).

Dimensions: H. 30.5 cm.

Description: Band of ivy leaves with dots below both figures. Dilute glaze: anatomical details. Red: both wreaths. Extensive preliminary sketch.

Condition: Broken and repaired. Some restoration in the figures, especially the bearded man on side B. On side A, the glaze on the neck of the amphora was applied in too thin a solution, giving it a reddish color.

Provenance: Formerly in Berlin, collection Prince Albert of Prussia, No. 911.

Bibliography: Verschiedener deutscher Kunstbesitz (Berlin, 27–29 May 1935) pl. 82; Beazley, *ARV*[2] 200, no. 51 and p. 1700; *Auction* 26 (5 October 1963) Münzen und Medaillen, Basel 68–9; von Bothmer, *MMA Exh* 4, no. 39; Beazley, *Paralipomena* 342.

C. B.

and beard are very similar to those of the dancer on this amphora.

Blacks, usually referred to by the Greeks as Ethiopians, were not unknown to the Athenians. Homer describes them as "blameless" and "dear to the gods" in the Iliad. Greater exposure was probably provided when Greek soldiers were employed as mercenaries for the Egyptians in the late seventh century. Ethiopians also formed part of Xerxes' army when he tried to conquer Greece in 480 B.C., but this probably post-dates the vase in question.

Both figures are dancing. Their poses are identical, indicating that they are perhaps dancing together, with each figure performing the same step simultaneously. Often the single figures on either side of vases by the Berlin Painter are involved in a common action. The youth holds a kylix in his outstretched left arm and swings the right be-

46. Red-Figure Nolan Amphora

Attic. Attributed to the Berlin Painter. Ca. 480 B.C. *Stoddard Collection. Yale University Art Gallery 1913.133.*

On Side A Athena stands in profile left on a simple strip of key pattern. She holds a spear in one hand and her helmet outstretched in the other. Her chiton is pleated in the center and adorned with dots, and over it she wears a himation which falls in loose but schematized folds. Her aegis has the same dot motif as the chiton and is bordered by a row of snakes. Her hair with a conspicuous wave in front is gathered in a roll at the nape of the neck and crowned by a simple diadem. A necklace and a bracelet on each arm are her other ornaments.

On Side B Hermes stands in profile in a pose similar to Athena although he faces right. An identical strip of key pattern runs under his feet. He grasps his outstretched caduceus in one hand. He is attired in a short himation, like Athena's, patterned with dots, a loose chiton gathered at one shoulder, and boots with a curling frontpiece. A petasos fastened by a string around his neck hangs at his back. His hair is short, bordered by red dots along the forehead and nape of the neck and crowned by a wreath. A faint moustache connects with the well-groomed beard which juts outward at the chin.

The use of single figure decoration characterized much late archaic vase painting, but the tendency to simplify, also manifest in the sparse ornament and static postures on this vase, reached its fullest expression in the work of the Berlin Painter. The tall slender shape of the amphora was particularly suited to large single figure decoration, and it is not surprising that it was the Berlin Painter's preferred shape. In order to accommodate the figures to the width of the amphora as well as to the height, he often represented standing figures with outstretched hands holding large objects in the manner of Athena and Hermes.

The works of the Berlin Painter follow the general progression during the late archaic period from highly schematized to increasingly naturalistic renderings. In the Berlin Painter's *oeuvre* this transition, expressed primarily in the treatment of drapery and the general feeling for design, is inseparably linked to a parallel trend toward less careful execution. J. D. Beazley has divided the Berlin Painter's *oeuvre* into early, middle, and late works and has assigned this vase to the middle period. The precisionist's love of pattern, the ex-

treme finesse of execution, and the exquisite grace of the Berlin Painter's finest productions of the first two decades of the century are absent here. The figures, like those on other works of the middle period are more massive, more conventional, and more inactive than their predecessors. In addition, their stance seems to be posed in a manner not seen heretofore. The reduced detail on garments and drapery, the less precise linear definition of attributes, well illustrated by Hermes' caduceus, the uneven application of the black ground, the inexplicable dilute glaze lines near and around Hermes' armhole, and the smudge of dilute glaze on Athena's neck bear witness to the less exact and less elegant execution of the middle period works. The haphazard rendering of the palmettes is yet a more forceful illustration of the change in quality between the Berlin Painter's early and middle works and might perhaps suggest another hand.

In the late works the manner of executing the figures sinks to the level of the neck decoration on the Yale vase. Although rendered in more active poses than those in the middle works, the figures tend to be more awkward and frozen in their attitudes. The extremely careless execution and the similarities to works by pupils and contemporaries increases the difficulty, which first arises with the middle works, of distinguishing the master's works from the productions by his school. This does not appear to be the case with the Yale amphora. Indeed, the figures are less graceful and on the whole less careful than the master's best productions and the simplification of patterning on the garments and the loosening of the drapery similarly separate it from his early productions. At the same time, it is more careful than the later works. The firm stance and dignified posture of the figures endow them with a nobility which is lacking in some of the more awkward middle works and the uninspired late productions.

Despite disparities caused by more or less careful execution and changes in certain stylistic conventions such as redition of drapery, the Berlin Painter's scheme for expressing anatomy in linear patterns varies little during his long activity. The Yale vase embodies many of these conventions. Perhaps the most prominent are the modes for depicting musculature in dilute glaze: two arcs convex to one another mark the biceps and triceps, two or three long lines the forearm, and a small arc the elbow; a wide curve outlines the calf, two lines the muscles of the leg, an arc and a smaller arc beneath it the knees, and two lines the muscles

46, Side A

46, Side B

of the neck. Two curving black lines indicate the ankle. The profile of the face tends to be upright, the chin full, the nostril a deep black arc and the eye long and often open at the inner end with a black dot for the iris.

This vase provides an early example of the image of the peaceful Athena with helmet in hand, a type which first appeared in the Late Archaic period.

The type was particularly popular from approximately 480 to 450 B.C., and perhaps served as a symbol of Athens' developing political self-confidence after the battle of Marathon.

Dimension: H. 32.7 cm.

Description: The neck has a double row of upright and inverted palmettes with interlacing tendrils on Side A and a single row of the same

47

47

palmette pattern with an additional egg pattern below on Side B. An inverted palmette with tendrils lies beneath each handle. Preliminary sketch: Side A—Athena's neck, jaw line, hair roll, legs, feet, arms, helmet, himation, and chiton. Side B—Hermes' face, beard, neck, legs, feet, arms, and himation. Dilute glaze: Side A—Athena's diadem, hair roll, part of hair, necklace, dots on aegis and chiton, line parallel to border of himation, sleeves of himation. Side B—Hermes' moustache, dots bordering hairline, neck, arm and leg muscles, border of right armhole. Red: Side A—fillet of hair roll, bracelets. Side B—wreath, string of petasos, boot ties.

Condition: Chip on mouth. Side A—chips on neck and inside left handle, pre-firing dent and loss of glaze below left sleeve of Athena, loss of glaze on folds of chiton below knee and on one portion of key pattern, crack below rib of right handle. Side B—slight dent, chip, and loss of glaze to right of Hermes' caduceus, chip above left boot.

Bibliography: Beazley, *VA* 38; J. C. Hoppin, *A Handbook of Attic Red-Figured Vases* (Cambridge, Mass. 1919) 63, no. 30; Jay Hambidge, *Dynamic Symmetry: The Greek Vase* (New Haven 1920) 57; Baur, *Stoddard Catalogue* 89–90, pl. 8; J. D. Beazley, *Attische Vasenmaler des rotifiguren Stils* (Tübingen 1925) 80, no. 44; Frederick Poulsen, *Aus einer alten Etruskerstadt* (Copenhagen 1927) pl. 10, 17; J. D. Beazley, *Der Berliner Maler* (Berlin 1930) 17, no. 53; Beazley, *ARV*² 201, no. 71, p. 219; Buitron, *NEC* 82–83, no. 39.

C. O.

47. Fragments of a Red-Figure Hydria

Attic. Attributed to the Berlin Painter. Ca. 475–465 B.C. Lent by Mr. and Mrs. Walter Bareiss; Bareiss No. 29.

These fragments from a hydria by the Berlin Painter provide an unusual example in his work of a scene in which two figures are depicted on the same side of the vase. Although only the upper portions of the figures survive, they clearly represent Athena proffering her helmet to a youth.

The pose of Athena on this vase, produced late in the Berlin Painter's career, is virtually identical with that on the Yale amphora attributed to the same artist (cat. no. 46). In each the goddess is holding her helmet with one hand and a spear in the other. The young man is also armed with two spears and a sword slung around his neck, which suggests that he is going off to battle. Athena offers him her helmet, perhaps as protection, and the youth reaches forward to grasp it.

Athena was not only the goddess of war, but also the helper and protectress of heroes. The image of her as an armed goddess seems to date from the second quarter of the sixth century and soon becomes the conventional type of representation. But when the goddess is shown with one of her favorites, she often acquires a more gentle and maternal quality, in spite of her military accoutrements.

The young man seems to be an anonymous soldier going off to war. It is possible, however, that he may represent the young Theseus, a favorite of Athena and the legendary hero of Athens, who was believed to have reappeared to aid Athenians in their fight against the Persians.

There is a gradual progression in the Berlin Painter's style from the highly schematized and precise renderings of his early period to the more naturalistic approach of his later works. The draughtsmanship in his late vases often becomes less precise and careful, and the line now seems thin and brittle. The poses of the figures seem quieter and more composed, with less of the taut springing energy of those on the Berlin Painter's earlier works. In this vase, the artist has paid far less attention to the rendering of the internal anatomical details and uses dilute glaze primarily for the decoration of Athena's drapery.

Dimensions: Max. pres. H. 21.0 cm.; max. pres. W. 32.8 cm.

Description: Meanders and saltire crosses below the scene. Dilute glaze: youth's long lock of hair, some anatomical detail (arms), decoration of Athena's drapery.

Condition: Series of fragments; missing pieces are restored and painted.

Bibliography: Beazley, *Paralipomena* 345, no. 183.

C. B.

48. Red-Figure Kylix

Attic. Manner of the Chaire Painter. Ca. 500 B.C. Stoddard Collection. Yale University Art Gallery 1913.162.

The striding jumper wears a wreath and holds a weight—a *halter*—in each hand. The Greeks practiced only the long jump, in which they carried lead weights of from four to eight pounds; the type

48

seen here were fitted with grooves for the fingers. The long jump was considered the most difficult of the five events of the pentathlon because of the problems inherent in the exercise; success depended upon exact coordination of the movements of arms and legs at the moment of take-off. The correct employment of the *halteres* required precision and control in the swing of the arms but enabled the exceptional athlete to clear over fifty feet in two jumps. The jumper represented here is at the end of his run and is about to leap. The rapid movement of the jumper is conveyed by the curling locks of his hair which stream backward— a realistic detail characteristic of the style of Greek drawing around 500 B.C.

During the last two decades of the sixth century the kylix was the most popular form among Attic red-figure vase painters; the interior tondo offered ample scope for experimentation. The single human figure became the dominant subject: revelers, satyrs, warriors, and athletes were isolated within homely, generic scenes which often, as here, encouraged the study of movement. Perhaps such scenes celebrating the pursuits of the common man reflected the change in socio-political institutions and attitudes which followed upon the overthrow of the Peisistratid Tyrants.

The most taxing visual problem presented by the figure of the jumper arises from the unlikely placement of his arms and the twist of his torso. Actually he is seen from behind and extends both weights in front of him. From the black-figure tradition the painter has inherited the formula of representing the head and limbs in profile; in a manner typical of the new interest in foreshortening and complicated poses, however, he has treated the waist as a pivot for twisting movement and rendered the back in three-quarter view. Still, depth in space is implied primarily by the overlapping of the left leg and the left arm. Closely related to the work of the Chaire Painter, this cup exhibits an ambitious pentagonal composition, characterized by restraint in detail and a vivid, forthright style. It reflects the influence of Epiktetos, one of the great masters of the period. The single figure adapted to the circular field, the oblique view, and the posture of the attenuated legs and arms are all conventional formulae among painters of the Epiktetan group.

Dimensions: D. 17.8 cm.

Description: Preliminary sketch lines used to define general contours of figure. Pentimenti evident only at heel of right foot, which was originally placed further to the right. Glaze used throughout, except on interiors of handles. Two reserved bands define tondo. Hair contour reserved. Relief lines used for general outline, facial features, fingers, and spine. Dilute glaze: ground line, prominent anatomical features and musculature: Red: wreath and four meaningless letters in field.

Condition: Assembled from several pieces. Large section of rim and left handle reconstructed. Foot and stem alien but ancient (probably from a Little Master cup). Int.: slight salt damage.

Provenance: Acquired in Rome.

Bibliography: Baur, *Stoddard Catalogue*, 107–8, no. 162, fig. 38; Beazley, *ARV*^{2} 145.

W. T. O.

49. Red-Figure Lekythos

Attic. The Bowdoin Painter. Early fifth century B.C. *Stoddard Collection. Yale University Art Gallery 1913.144.*

The Bowdoin Painter, identified by J. D. Beazley on the basis of two lekythoi at Bowdoin College, is a painter of small vases that are usually decorated with a single figure. He was a prolific painter— over two hundred vases are attributed to him and his style is accordingly rather rough and hasty. Vases attributed to the Bowdoin Painter are usually repetitive in subject matter, often representing a woman engaged in some domestic activity or a flying Nike. Characteristic features of his technique are a continuous line for the nose and forehead which extends into the hair, a long eye with a curved upper and straight lower lid, and the omission of relief contour for the lips.

The lekythos, a one-handled jug for oils and unguents, was often used as an offering for the dead. The decoration of this vase, a sphinx seated on a small pedestal, confirms such usage in this particular case. The sphinx, a creature with a woman's head, lion's body, serpent's tail, and eagle's wings, was originally imported from the east and occurs frequently in black-figure vase painting (see for example the black-figure loutrophoros in this exhibition, cat. no. 27). Although the sphinx is usually associated with the well-known myth of Oedipus, it also has a broader significance in Greek mythology and imagery. Occasional early representations of the sphinx as a demon of death in scenes of battle were superseded in the sixth century by its more common depiction as a benign symbol of death and separation. Sphinxes often appear on top of grave stelae and on vessels used for funeral purposes. The three steps of the pedestal and the stylized bush also follow traditional conventions for grave monuments in vase painting.

Unfortunately, the damaged condition of this vase tends to obscure the appealing qualities of the Bowdoin Painter's style. Although neither the draughtsmanship nor the subject is remarkable, vases by the Bowdoin Painter have a freshness and simplicity which are quite pleasing. The only other known lekythos by the Bowdoin Painter with a sphinx is in the National Museum, Athens (1938, Beazley, *ARV*² 685, no. 166).

Dimensions: H. 17.7 cm.

Description: Type II lekythos. Key pattern below the scene. Five black palmettes on reserved shoulder; tongue patterns at base of the neck. Red: fillet.

Condition: Broken and repaired; large section of the upper back of vessel and the outer ends of the sphinx's wings restored; surface pitted.

Provenance: From Laurion.

Bibliography: Baur, *Stoddard Catalogue* 97–8, fig. 31; Beazley, *ARV*² 685, no. 167. On the subject, see Hans Walter, "Sphingen," *Antike und Abenland* 9 (1960) 63–72.

C. B.

50. Red-Figure Lekythos

Attic. Manner of the Providence Painter. Ca. 460 B.C. Stoddard Collection. Yale University Art Gallery 1913.148.

Boreas, God of the North Wind, was a patron of Athens because, according to legend, he had abducted Oreithyia, daughter of the Athenian king, Erectheus, as his bride. The Athenians also credited Boreas with the storm that sank the fleet of Xerxes off the coast of Thessaly in 480 B.C., and proceeded to build a temple in his honor (Herodotus VII, 189).

The events probably explain the increasing popularity of images of Boreas during the first half of the fifth century B.C. The god is shown on vases as a winged diety whose principal characteristic is velocity. Essential attributes are his beard, wings, chiton, and running posture. The typical scene involving Boreas depicts the abduction of Oreithyia; the Yale lekythos is unusual in that only Boreas is shown.

49

50

The Providence Painter was an Attic artist active in the early and mid-Classic periods of Greek vase painting. Beazley thought that he was trained by the Berlin Painter. Most of the Providence Painter's vases are small pieces, principally Nolan amphorae and lekythoi. The Yale lekythos is not close enough in style or technical mastery to be the work of the Providence Painter himself but was conceivably a workshop piece. The statuesque figure of Boreas, precise sharp lines for the details of the face, and fluid, almost calligraphic lines for the rest of the body are characteristic of the Providence Painter's style. Particular traits of the painter that are visible on the figure of Boreas are: wide open eye with arc-shaped lower lid, three-quarter circle ear, strong chin, U-shaped ankle motif, aquiline nose slightly turned up at the tip, compact coiffure, rounded fingers and toes with no nails, and excessively foreshortened arms and legs.

Dimensions: H. 21.3 cm.

Description: Four black palmettes on reserved red shoulder, ring of black dots above them; leftward meander above scene, in front; reserved line encircles the vase below. Red wash on mouth, neck, shoulder and foot. Dilute glaze: wing details.

Condition: Broken at neck and handle and repaired with small fragments missing. Some surface wear.

Bibliography: Baur, *Stoddard Catalogue,* 99–100, fig. 31; Beazley, *ARV*² 645, 6.

D. T.

51. Red-Figure Kylix

Attic. Attributed to the Brygos Painter. Ca. 490–480 B.C. Lent by Mr. and Mrs. Walter Bareiss; Bareiss no. 53.

The Brygos Painter is one of the most skillful and prolific of the Ripe Archaic Cup Painters. He is fond of scenes with a great deal of motion and usually decorates his cups and vases with running and dancing figures, delighting in the chance to display his sure knowledge of anatomy and his love of the flowing rhythm of drapery. This, combined with his attention to detail and the alert expression of his figures, gives an exuberant charm and infectious *joie de vivre,* especially to his early cups.

The decoration of this kylix is restricted to the interior. The tondo is filled with the form of a woman fleeing to the left while looking back at her

51

pursuer. Her right arm is flung behind her, perhaps in a gesture of supplication, while her left holds up a fillet or sash. To the left the chiton swings out behind her to fill the lower part of the tondo, while the thicker, blanket-like himation over her shoulders fills the upper level.

The Brygos Painter is a master in the depiction of drapery. He emphasizes the contrast between the closely placed pleats of the thin transparent chiton and the broader folds of the heavier himation by the use of the thick black border on the edge of the himation. Yet in spite of the naturalism of the drapery, its primary function is decorative; it swells and swings in order to bring the exaggerated pose of the running figure into full and complete harmony with difficult formal demands of the roundel.

As in many of his vase paintings, the Brygos Painter adds various details in reddish dilute glaze.

The hair of this figure is blonde, and various details, such as the zig-zag pattern on her cap and the string holdings the chiton, are also painted with dilute glaze.

Beazley has stated that most of the cups painted only on the interior are late in the Brygos Painter's career. But the vigorous drawing, the strong sense of motion, and the beautifully expressive rendering of the face and hands suggest that it was produced at the high point of the painter's *oeuvre*.

Dimensions: D. of bowl 21.6 cm.

Description: Type B kylix. Undecorated exterior. Tondo framed by band of rightward meanders and cross-squares. Dilute glaze: hair, patterns on cap, and waist string.

Condition: Broken and repaired. Large area of restoration in lower right center of interior. Surface flaked and abraded.

Bibliography: von Bothmer, *MMA Exh* 7, no.

52

89; Beazley, *Paralipomena* 367. On the artist: Beazley, *ARV*² 244–56; Alexander Cambitoglou, *The Brygos Painter* (Sydney 1968); Max Wegner, *Brygosmaler* (Berlin 1973).

C. B.

52. Red-Figure Kylix

Attic. Late work by the Brygos Painter. 480–470 B.C. Stoddard Collection. Yale University Art Gallery 1913.164.

This kylix is decorated on the interior only, with a figural tondo framed by a meander pattern. Within the tondo a youthful musician stands before a flaming altar. He plays the double flute and carries a provision basket on his back. The figure is nude, except for a himation draped over his left shoulder. He leans backward slightly, supporting himself against a staff. The word *kalos*, "beautiful," is inscribed twice in the field.

The double flute player, as he occurs on our vase, is a very common Brygan motif, appearing often in both scenes of symposia and in Dionysiac revels. Indicative of the Brygos Painter's style is the economy of line with which the figure is drawn, particularly evident in the graceful hands, with fingers widely spaced and gingerly grasping the flute. He depicts natural motions and anatomical essentials with a deftly drawn line.

The face of the flutist conforms to the Brygan mold, with nose turned up slightly at the end and the line from forehead to nose slightly concave.

The nostril is represented by a short curve and the eyebrow forms a long arch above the left eye. Features such as the strong, rounded chin, serrated lower edge of the hair, and bushy sideburns correspond to those of the youth on the interior tondo of a kylix in Würzburg (P.E. Arias and Max Hirmer, *1000 Years of Greek Vase Painting* [New York 1962] pl. 33).

The Yale kylix is a late work by the Brygos Painter, classified as such both on the basis of its lack of exterior painting (Beazley, *ARV*² 251) and because the broad, naturalistic treatment of the drapery indicates Late Archaic/Early Classical tradition (ca. 480–470 B.C.). The fold formations of the Yale figure's drapery resemble those of other late cups by the Brygos Painter (Compare the drapery of figures on a cup formerly in Manchester and on a fragmentary cup in Munich. See Alexander Cambitoglou, *The Brygos Painter* [Sydney 1968] 39 and pl. XVII, no. 2).

The Brygos Painter was one of a second generation of red-figure artists who painted during the ripe archaic period, ca. 500–475 B.C. He was primarily a kylix painter, although he occasionally decorated kantharoi, rhyta, kyathoi or ladles, Nolan amphorae, lekythoi, oinchoai, and skyphoi.

The Brygos Painter decorated his vases with such diverse subjects as episodes from Homeric epics, scenes from mythology, Dionysiac revels, and merrymaking at symposia. The symposion was one of his favorite subjects, and it is perhaps to such scenes that the Yale kylix relates most closely. The young musician with the provision basket on his back is a type of performer typically seen at Brygan banquets.

Dimension: H. 9.5 cm.; D. 20.7 cm.

Description: Type B kylix. Reddish fabric with lustrous black glaze. The contours of the figure are painted in relief line, except for the upper portion of the hair. Sideburns painted in dilute glaze. Wreath, strings of provision basket, flames of altar, and inscriptions in field are painted red. Faintly inscribed guidelines near contours of figure.

Inscriptions: ΚΑΛΟΣ (twice)

Condition: Broken and mended. Portion of rim repaired. Figural design complete, except for slight damage around eye and partial effacement of interior washes by prior cleaning.

Bibliography: Baur, *Stoddard Catalogue* 108–9, pl. 14; Beazley, *ARV*² 377, 105. On the artist: Alexander Cambitoglou, *The Brygos Painter* (Sydney 1968); Max Wegner, *Brygosmaler* (Berlin 1973). J. K.

53. Red-Figure Column Krater

Attic. Attributed to the Arigento Painter. Ca. 475–450 B.C. Gift of Allison V. Armour, B. A. 1884. Yale University Art Gallery 1933.175.

The column krater, with its full body and broad mouth, was used for mixing wine and water. The shape of the Yale vase is characteristic; the flaring lip and the foot in two degrees are standard, as are the handles, made up of pairs of cylindrical stems, for which the form is named.

In the second quarter of the fifth century, a regular scheme for the decoration of the column krater is established. Conventionalized lotus, palmette, and ivy patterns occupy the lip and neck of the vase, and the figural scenes on the body of the krater are typically set within frames of conventionalized ivy and tongue pattern. A ray pattern extends upward from the foot.

Side A shows two male figures in two pairs. The first figure raises his left hand in a stylized conversational attitude; his right hand, in which he holds an apple, is extended toward the second figure. The third figure, like the first, takes the initiative in the conversation; in his left hand, which is raised, he holds a hare. Both No. 1 and No. 3 are older than No. 2 and No. 4; No. 1 is bearded, and both are taller than their counterparts. Between the second and third figures a strigil, or oil-scraper, serves as a space filler.

As is customary for the period, the figures on Side B of the vase are of less importance than those on A and consequently are less carefully executed. Side B shows three male figures, one, in the center, similar to No. 2 and No. 4 on A, two with lowered himations and walking sticks, like No. 1 and No. 3 on A.

Both sides of the krater depict male courting scenes. The iconographic tradition to which such scenes belong dates from the second quarter of the sixth century. Black-figure courting scenes are explicitly sexual, but with the introduction of the red-figure style comes a new sense of decorum. Figures are consistently draped, and there is an increased emphasis on the expression of the action through traditional symbols. The hare and the apple, both sacred to Aphrodite, signify lust. The hare, in particular, is associated with pederasty.

The Agrigento painter was one of a group of mannerists, members of a single workshop, active ca. 475 to ca. 450. The Yale vase clearly belongs to the mannerist tradition. The poses of figures No. 1 and No. 3 on A and figure No. 3 on B, in partic-

53, Side A

ular, reveal the theatricality typical of mannered work, while figure No. 3 on A shows the characteristically mannered combination of profile arms and legs with frontal torso. The flattening of the drapery into surface pattern, the lack of anatomical detail, the absence of any apparent interest in foreshortening also link the Yale vase with the work of the mannerists.

Dimensions: H. 39 cm.; D. at mouth 26 cm.; D. at handles 34 cm.

Description: Preliminary sketch: Side A— Figures No. 1 and No. 3 in the area of the legs; in addition, some apparently haphazard marks on the face and upper body of these and other figures. Dilute glaze: Side A—the spotted body of the hare and certain of the facial features. Red: Side A—

53, Side B, detail

fillets of figures Nos. 2, 3 and 4; Side B—fillets of figure No. 1 and No. 2.

Inscription: There is a *kalos* inscription on either side of the vase, between figures No. 3 and No. 4 on A and between figures No. 2 and No. 3 on B.

Condition: The vase has never been repaired or restored. There is some minor damage from chlorides on both sides. A curious feature of the condition of the piece is the continuous line that occurs on the lower body—probably the result of conditions of production in the workshop where the vase was made.

Provenance: Found in the vicinity of Taranto; formerly in the collection of Thomas B. Clarke.

Bibliography: American Art Association Galleries, Sale Catalogue Jan. 4, 1917, no. 373; Paul V. C. Baur, "The Armour Kelebe," *Bulletin of the Associates in Fine Arts at Yale University* 7 (1936) 10–11; Beazley, *ARV*² 576, no. 45.

E. B.

54. Red-Figure Oinochoe

Attic. Name vase of the Yale Oinochoe Painter. Ca. 470–460 B.C. Stoddard Collection. Yale University Art Gallery 1913.143.

Poseidon on the left, wearing a black-bordered himation and holding a trident in his left hand greets Theseus, who is dressed for travel, wearing a black-bordered chlamys and a petasos, and holding two spears in his left hand.

J. D. Beazley ascribes twenty-eight pots and fragments to the Yale Oinochoe Painter of which the largest number (ten) are stamnoi. Among the more notable examples in his *oeuvre* are a hydria in the Fogg Art Museum (1960.340) depicting women feeding herons and a bell-krater in the Louvre (G 368) showing Triptolemos and Demeter. Both pots echo the serenity and nobility of the composition on the Yale oinochoe.

The tall, loosely-defined, statuesque figures of Poseidon and Theseus seem to reflect stylistic developments which are associated with the renowned mural painters Polygnotos and Mikon, whose works are known only through literary descriptions. In keeping with the nature of the early free style, particularly the example set by one of the most prominent painters of the time, the Niobid Painter, figures are rendered with a concern for the expression of inward consciousness and character (*ethos*). The eyes shown in full profile, the rendering of hair with a greater emphasis on separate strands, and drapery which reflects the play of underlying forms help to secure the dating of the oinochoe to the second quarter of the fifth century.

While depictions of Poseidon greeting Theseus do not occur in black-figure vase painting, several other versions in red-figure are known. The encounter seems to be part of a story recorded by the poet Bacchylides in which Minos, the King of Crete, challenged Theseus to prove that Poseidon was his father by retrieving a gold ring from the sea. Theseus sprang overboard and, aided by dolphins, reached Poseidon's undersea palace, where the sea-god's wife, Amphitrite, gave him a mantle and wreath. Wearing these gifts he reappeared before Minos. Earlier versions of the Poseidon-Theseus meeting are found on a calyx krater in the Bibliothèque Nationale, Paris (418), attributed to the Syriskos Painter, and on a column krater in the Fogg Art Museum (1960.339) attributed to the Harrow Painter. These allude more explicitly to the story by including such details as a Nereid and the throne of Poseidon, in the former, and a mantle and wreath, in the latter. The Yale Oinochoe Painter's departure from the more traditional depiction of the encounter may suggest a more symbolic intention.

During the first half of the fifth century B.C. Theseus came to be regarded as a semi-divine guardian of Athens and an embodiment of its patriotic spirit. Tradition held that he had appeared on the battlefield of Marathon to aid the Athenians, and after what were thought to be his bones were brought from Scyros to Athens by Cimon in 474–473 B.C., a cult was established in his honor

(Plutarch, *Life of Theseus*, 35–36). Theseus thus became a symbol of Athens as well as a character in legend, and it seems probable that his images. which grew in popularity during the fifth century, took on a political as well as a narrative significance. On our vase the armed Theseus shaking hands with Poseidon may symbolize the fact that the power and prosperity of Athens after the Persian Wars were based to a great degree on alliances which gave it control of the sea.

Dimensions: H. 40.3 cm.

Description: While the pot is covered with a poorly fired inferior glaze over a brownish-red fabric, the bottom and edge of the disc-shaped foot, which is painted red, are unglazed. There is also a reserved ring where the foot joins the body. On the lip is an egg pattern and below the figures is a triple rightward meander.

Condition: Repaired but complete. A horizontal break cuts across the center of the two figures; a diagonal crack passes through the upper portion of the body of Theseus and another through his face. A small piece of Poseidon's drapery at the thigh has been repainted as has a thin line across the face of Theseus.

Bibliography: Baur, *Stoddard Catalogue* 96, no. 143; Beazley, *VA* 61; Beazley, *ARV*² 503, no. 25; Brommer, *Vasenlisten* 145, no. 4; Buitron, *NEC* no. 59; Joseph C. Hoppin, *A Handbook of Attic Red-figure Vases* (Cambridge, Mass. 1919) II, 484, no. 6.

R. S.

55. Red-Figure Hydria

Attic. Probably by the Aegisthus Painter, Ca. 470 B.C. Lent by Mr. and Mrs. Walter Bareiss, Bareiss no. 27.

Herakles wrestling the Nemean Lion, the earliest of the Twelve Labors, is a common subject on black-figure vases. Two poses for the combat are established relatively early in the black-figure series and continue basically intact into the limited number of red-figure representations of the subject. In the more common black-figure pose, which appears to be the earlier type, Herakles is standing with one or both arms locked around the lion, who is balanced on his hind legs. This type also occurs on sculpture, as, for example, the metopes from the Hephaisteon in Athens and the Treasury of the Athenians in Delphi (Frank Brommer, *Herakles*

[Münster/Cologne 1953] pls. 2 and 6). Herakles often attacks the lion with a dagger or sword in the vertical format scenes (Frank Brommer, *Herakles* 8, pl. 5, and Haspels, *ABL* 117 note 1).

The second type, for which no sculptural prototype or parallel seems to survive, is in horizontal format. As on this kalpis, Herakles kneels to the left with his arms locked around the head of the lion who is crouched on all fours to the right. In a relatively frequent variant, the lion has a hind foot on Herakles' head. This type is found most frequently on the shoulders of hydriae and lekythoi, as well as on the predellas of amphorae, although both types do occur on most vase shapes.

On this vase, Herakles is shown as a young bearded man. Apparently without strain, he has caught the lion's head in his left arm, which can be seen behind and below the lion's ruff. The lion's paw appears on Herakles' right shoulder. A thin, bent tree defines the exterior space and helps enclose the composition at the top. It also echoes Herakles' pose, as the lion's pose is repeated by his tail. A band of meanders and crosses provides the ground line for the combat. The onlookers common in black-figure representations are excluded here. This isolation of the episode is closer to sculptural versions than to earlier black-figure prototypes.

The Aegisthus Painter, to whom Beazley attributes this kalpis, painted large pots in the early free style (ca. 475–450 B.C.). Very few mythological subjects by his hand survive; komos, symposion, or pursuit scenes, and stock scenes of one or two standing figures are more usual. His style seems to derive from the later works of the Copenhagen and Syriskos Painters (Beazley, *ARV*² 256). Particularly close is a hydria by the Syriskos Painter in London with Herakles and the Lion (British Museum E 168, *CVA* 73,3 and 74, 2–4). That version appears the earlier of the two. The Syriskos Painter's composition is framed by Athena, Iolaos, and two warriors in the tradition of black-figure representations. The Aegisthus Painter adopts the more expressive convention of the circle with a dot for the pupil of the eye, where his predecessor retains the solid black pupil. A freer drawing style and more energetic poses characterize the younger artist's work while the Syriskos Painter's figures still show the restraint of the late works of Douris.

Dimensions: H. 27.9 cm.

Description: Type II hydria (kalpis). Dilute glaze: lion's mane, ribs, and the line defining Herakles' lip. Preliminary sketch virtually complete.

54

55

Pairs of one leftward and one rightward meander alternate with cross-squares below.

    Condition: Broken and repaired.

    Bibliography: von Bothmer, *MMA Exh* no. 57; Beazley, *Paralipomena* 381.

S. M. B.

56. Red-Figure Lekythos

Attic. Name vase of the Yale Lekythos Painter. Ca. 475–450 B.C. Stoddard Collection. Yale University Art Gallery 1913.146.

This lekythos is a handsome example of early free style vase painting. The style is characterized by a broader and ampler conception of the human figure, a greater feeling for the development of space, and a new sense of realism.

    The scene depicts a woman folding a garment before placing it in a chest. She stands beside a chair, and on the wall behind her hang a mirror on the left and a wreath on the right. Greek clothing, which was usually rectangular in shape, was often folded and kept in large chests such as the one illustrated on this vase.

    Scenes from daily life were introduced by Late Archaic vase painters early in the fifth century and

56

by the second quarter of the century became more common than the mythological scenes that had dominated earlier vase painting. Usually the type of subject reflects in some way the purpose of the vase, and in this case the quiet and simple evocation of daily life underlines the function of the lekythos as a vase used in the home as well as for funereal purposes.

The realism of the subject is enhanced by the naturalism of the figure and the drapery. The eye is now drawn in profile rather than in full-front view, and the peplos falls in broad heavy folds quite distinct from those of the chiton underneath. A new interest in spatial development is suggested by the position of the woman in front of the chair, indicating an attempt to penetrate the field and give some suggestion of depth. Most remarkable, however, is the new breadth and monumentality given the human form.

There are seventy-eight pieces attributed to the Yale Lekythos Painter, most of which are decorated with women involved in domestic activities. His style is loose and sketchy, and he is typical of his generation in the static arrangement and contemplative tone of his forms. This vase, with its beautifully balanced composition, is the high-point of his *ouevre*.

Dimensions: H. 33.9 cm.

Description: Above and below the scene a band of alternating pairs of right and leftward meanders separated by dotted saltire crosses. Three palmettes on the shoulder. Egg and dart at base of neck.

Condition: Broken and repaired. Restored along break lines.

Bibliography: Beazley, *VA* 72–4; Beazley, *ARV²* 658, no. 30; for the artist see 657–62; J. D. Beazley, *Attische Vasenmaler des rotifiguren Stils* (Tübingen 1925) 143–45.

C. B.

57. Red-Figure Amphora

Attic. Attributed to the Painter of the Boston Phiale. Ca. 450–420 B.C. Stoddard Collection. Yale University Art Gallery 1913.134.

The shape of the vase is typical of the later variety of the Nolan amphora. The echinus lip, the unglazed disc-shaped foot, the handles with a central ridge, and the streamlined body are characteristic.

Side A shows a pursuit scene. The young man on the right wears the short chiton, the chlamys fastened at the shoulder with a clasp, and the petasos. Striations on the foot represent boots. In his left hand he carries two spears.

The woman fleeing to the left wears her hair, held in place by *taeniae,* or bands of cloth, in a knot on the back of her head. A short mantle conceals her left hand; with her right she pulls at the shoulder of her chiton. This gesture usually means "wife or bride of"; perhaps in this case it anticipates the outcome of the action.

The decorative border of meander and cross patterns beneath the figures is a feature of the later Nolan amphorae.

Side B shows the solitary figure of a woman

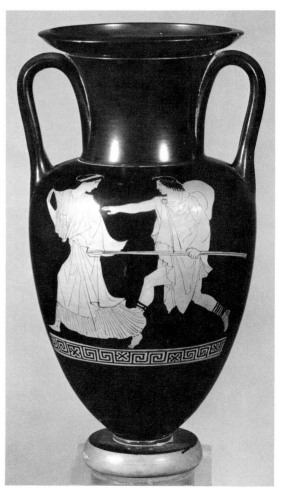

57, Side A

57, Side B, detail

wrapped in a mantle. Like the female figure on A, she wears the radiated *taeniae*. Her mouth is open, a convention indicating emotion, and her expression can be read as a response to the action on the other side of the vase. Similar mantled figures occur on the B side of a considerable number of Nolan amphorae.

During the fifth century, the theme of the pursuit becomes increasingly popular. The pose of the male figure becomes standardized with one arm extended, the other lowered. In some instances, attributes such as the caduceus of Hermes and the trident of Poseidon replace the spears and serve to identify the figures.

The prevalence of pursuit scenes has lead to the identification of types. J. D. Beazley suggests that the male figure on the Phiale Painter amphora may be Theseus (*ARV*² 1015). The revival of interest in the Thesiad that took place in the fifth century resulted in the development of a whole new iconography based on the various exploits of the hero. The figures on the Phiale Painter vase cannot, however, be positively identified; by the middle of the century the pursuit scene had become generic.

The Phiale Painter was a pupil of the Achilles Painter, perhaps the greatest artist of the period. Like his master, the Phiale Painter is strongly influenced by contemporary sculpture. Between ca. 480 and ca. 440, sculptors had made rapid progress toward the naturalistic representation of the running figure, and the Phiale vase reflects this progress. The idealized expressions of the figures likewise originate in sculpture.

The work of the Phiale Painter is in one sense

derivative, but his Nolan amphorae have a restrained elegance that makes them exceptional.

Dimensions: H. 33.8 cm.

Description: Preliminary sketch: Side A—marks on the face of the female figure suggest that the painter originally intended to make her taller; the right foot of the youth, too large in proportion to the leg, is drawn in the area where, in the finished work, it is hidden by the woman's flowing chiton. Relief contour throughout. Dilute glaze: Side A— the hairline of the female figure, details of anatomy of the male figure, the hems of the garments of both; Side B—the hem of the mantle and the folds of the chiton showing below. Red—Side A— *taeniae* of female figure and wreath of male.

Condition: The vase has never been repaired or restored. The glaze is the rich glaze characteristic of Nolan Amphorae—it has a slight greenish tinge, and there are occasional instances of misfiring. The color of the reserved red is somewhat uneven, especially on Side B; this condition can be ascribed to irregularities in the clay.

Bibliography: Beazley, *VA* 168, no. 14; *The Diagonal*, 1 (1919) 53, fig. 5a; J.C. Hoppin, *A Handbook of Attic Red-Figure Vases* I (Cambridge, Mass. 1919) 86, no. 25; Jay Hambidge, *Dynamic Symmetry* (New Haven 1920) 77, 79, fig. 5; Baur, *Stoddard Catalogue* 90, pl. 8; Beazley, *ARV*² 1015, no. 13.

E. B.

58. Red-Figure Owl Skyphos

Attic. Early fifth century B.C. *Stoddard Collection. Yale University Art Gallery 1913.161.*

The owl flanked by olive branches became common decoration on skyphoi during the first quarter of the fifth century. Its appearance at this time coincided with and relates to the spirit of civic pride and optimism that followed the Athenian victory over the Persians in the early years of the fifth century. The owl was the symbol of Athens as well as the personal attribute of Athena. Its association with the goddess dates from ca. 550 B.C. and is contemporary with the beginning of the image of Athena as an armed war goddess with shield and helmet. After 490 B.C., the olive wreath, also connected with Athena, frequently appears encircling her helmet.

Beginning with the early years of the tyranny of Peisistratus (mid-sixth century B.C.), owls are often

58

found associated with Athena and appear in sculpture and on coins. The latter were particularly influential in the propagation of the image as a symbol of the city of Athens, and in many cases depictions of owls on vases seem directly derived from the representations on coins. Aside from its political and symbolic overtones, however, the popularity of the owl was surely related to its charming and comic appearance.

Owl skyphoi were produced in large numbers and are usually rather carelessly made. They appear all through the fifth and into the fourth century, with some examples produced in Italy. The skyphos at Yale is very similar to an owl skyphos at the Metropolitan Museum in New York, also Type B (Museum Number 41.162.208). Both have wide touching eye circles, much the same arrangement of dots, and remarkably similar drawing of the eyebrows and wings.

Dimensions: H. 8.3 cm.; D. 15 cm. with handles.

Description: Type B skyphos (glaux): one horizontal, one vertical handle. On each side an owl facing right between two olive branches. Reserved band encircles the vase below the owls, serving as a ground line. Lustrous black glaze.

Condition: Intact, surface well preserved.

Bibliography: Baur, *Stoddard Catalogue* 107, fig. 90; George Lippold, "Vasen und Münzen," *JdI* 67 (1952) 93—98; J. H. Jonkees, "Notes on the Coinage of Athens: VIII: The Owl of Athens," *Mnemosyne*, 4th Series, No. 5 (1952) 28—41; Franklin P. Johnson, "An Owl Skyphos," *Studies Presented to David M. Robinson* (St. Louis 1953) 96–105 and "A Note on Owl Skyphoi," *AJA* 59 (1955) 119–124; on owl skyphoi, see Beazley, *ARV*^{2} 982.

C. B.

59. Red-Figure Oinochoe ("Chous")

Attic. Ca. 435 B.C. Stoddard Collection. Yale University Art Gallery 1913.139.

Squat oinochoai with low handles, wide trefoil mouths, and short necks which connect smoothly with fat, bulbous bodies are found in a wide range of sizes (cf. Yale 1913.142, H. 4.5 cm.). When full-sized, like the present vase, the Type III oinochoe or "chous" held a fixed volume, a "chous" or just over three liters. Though serving on the one hand as wine jugs in everyday use, vessels of this particular shape had a more specialized function. They played a part in the ritual activities on *Choes*, the second day of the Anthesteria, the great "Festival of Flowers" celebrated annually in Athens in late February-early March. Throughout this day of Dionysiac reveling, every individual, child and adult alike, carried his own oinochoe. A great wine feast culminated in a drinking contest in which each contestant strove to down a chous of wine most quickly. As Dikaiopolis says in Aristophanes' *Acharnians* upon winning the contest and coming to claim the promised skinful of wine: "After filling the pitcher with the unmixed wine I drank it down in one continuous draught." (line 1228).

The identification of the three figures on the vase is made difficult by the absence of inscriptions and the sparseness of distinguishing attributes. Various interpretations of the scene which have been made, Ion (?), Creusa (?), and Apollo (?) (Baur, 94) and the worship of a hero (Buschor, 316, followed by Karouzou, 123, and van Hoorn, 156), are necessarily speculative and inconclusive. In view of the function of the chous one may venture yet another hypothesis, namely, that the scene represents Erigone and Orestes before Apollo. The former two figure in folk aetiologies which explain activities at the Anthesteria. Orestes is the *aition* for the practice of requiring each participant to drink from his own cup. When the youth arrived in Athens for his trial after having killed his mother Clytemnestra, the city was in festival. So that he might participate and yet not contaminate the populace by his uncleanness, all were directed to drink from a separate cup (see Euripides, *Iphigenia in Tauris*, lines 947–60). Erigone was the *aition* for the Aiora or swing ceremony, a ritual which took place on the third day of the Anthesteria. In a presumably Athenian version of the story she was the daughter of Aegisthus and Clytemnestra who came to Athens to prosecute Orestes at his trial, pleading the case of her father. When her half-brother won his freedom, she hanged herself, and her death led to the initiation of the Aiora (*Etymologicum Magnum*; cf. Apollodoros, *Epitome*, VI,25). Apollo's connection is clear. The god, who may be identified by his laurel branch, originally instructed Orestes to kill his mother and was his defender at the trial.

The vase, though fragmentary, is seen to be of high quality. It is as yet unattributed. Ernst Buschor relates it to Louvre MNB, 1705 and to another oinochoe in the same museum (*Griechische Vasenmalerei*, 316). J.D. Beazley places it in the free style before ca. 420. Paul Baur's date, ca. 435 B.C., the time of the Eretria Painter and the last years of "Periclean Athens" when the Parthenon frieze was complete and the pediments were going up, is convincing. The piece shares compositional schemes and stylistic features with other choes of the period. The customary three figures are placed in a stark, metope-like panel surrounded by an ornamented frame. Here the frame consists of palmettes above, chevrons on the sides, and triple meanders alternating with checkered squares below, a scheme which conforms to Gerard van Hoorn's pattern "3". Interest is maintained through the poses of the figures, their gestures, and their glances. Drawing is delicate and expressive. All is subtle and refined.

Dimensions: H. 23.1 cm.

Description: Preliminary sketching visible. Muscles on youth's chest and alternate stripes on

59

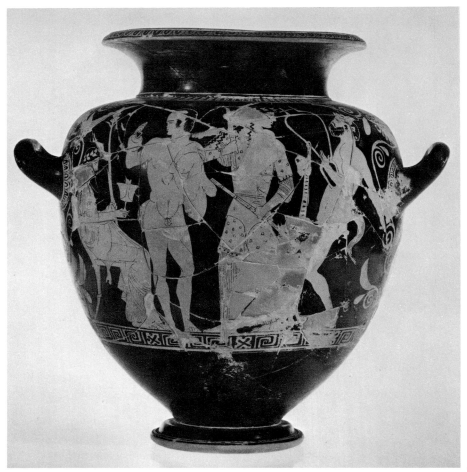

60, Side A

scabbard in dilute glaze. Handles and area beneath handle misfired.

Condition: Reconstructed from numerous fragments and restored. Extensive losses include face of woman, lower legs of central youth, head and left shoulder of right figure. Much of trefoil lip and entire base modern. Surface abrasion of left arm of central figure. General wearing of relief lines.

Bibliography: Beazley, *VA* 180; Baur, *Stoddard Catalogue* 94, fig. 32, pl. IX; Ernst Buschor in Adolf Furtwängler, Karl Reichhold, *Griechische Vasenmalerei*, III (Munich 1932) 316; David Moore Robinson, *CVA*, The Robinson Coll. fasc.

3, (Baltimore 1938) 19; Semni Papaspyridi Karouzou, "Chous," *AJA* 50 (1946) 123; Gerard van Hoorn, *Choes and Anthesteria* (Leiden 1951) 156.

E. S.

60. Red-Figure Stamnos

Attic. Attributed to the Midas Painter. Ca. 440 B.C. Stoddard Collection. Yale University Art Gallery 1913.132.

On Side A, Dionysos is seated on a high-backed chair at the left; he holds a thyrsos in his left hand

60, Side B

and a kantharos in his right, into which vessel a youthful, snub-nosed satyr pours wine from a trefoil-oinochoe. A maenad approaches the young satyr in a running-step, looking over her shoulder, dressed in a chiton with a fawn skin, and holding torches in her hands. To the extreme right, a bearded satyr esctatically strums a lyre from which hangs a flute-case, and he holds a plectrum in his right hand. The satyrs are nude and bald, and all but the young one are wreathed with ivy. On Side B, two satyrs, snub-nosed and bald, converse with upraised hands with a maenad resting statuesquely upon a tree-staff; she wears a *sakkos* over her hair, and is draped in a long-sleeved chiton. The sub-

ject matter on both sides of this vase is a most common one in the second half of the fifth century B.C. Scenes representing Dionysos and his thiasos become standardized and conventional. In the Classical period, the once frenzied dances of maenads and satyrs become moderate and restrained. Dionysos reclines rather quietly, or sits with stately dignity as seen on this stamnos, while maenads bring him food and drink, satyrs pour him wine, or play the lyre for his pleasure. Satyrs and maenads no longer romp with the erotic abandon characteristic of vases earlier than ca. 460 to ca. 430 B.C. but engage in tranquil conversations. Dionysos' thyrsos, a spear stuck through a pinecone, seems to sprout forth branches. This may be a reference to him as the tree-god or vine-god in the rural Dionysiac festivals.

The frequent appearance of stamnoi within some kind of cult-festival in scenes painted on stamnoi of the middle and later fifth century has led scholars to think of the stamnos as a cult vase for either of two Dionysiac festivals, the Anthesteria or the Lenaia. August Frickenhaus first associated the stamnos with the Lenaia (*Lenäenvasen* [Berlin 1912]) since, on stamnoi such as Boston 418 by the Chicago Painter, Louvre G408 and Oxford 523 by the Villa Giulia Painter, scenes of the Lenaia appear showing a herm of Dionysos, crowned with ivy, a pile of ritual cakes on a table in front of the image of the god, and two or more large stamnoi, from which maenads dip wine in skyphoi. Other maenads surround these scenes, dancing in ecstasy with thyrsoi, torches, and flutes. None of these attributes of the Lenaian cult appears on the Yale stamnos, and Barbara Philippaki in her monograph on the Attic stamnos believes that there is no reason to consider the stamnos a vase to Dionysos (Barbara Philippaki, *The Attic Stamnos* [Oxford 1967] p. XX). Anthesterian scenes presented on the fifth century stamnoi mentioned above would be an iconographic possibility, if the women consecrating the vessels of wine on these stamnoi were priestesses; but, just as on the Yale stamnos, they are clearly maenads.

Satyrs and maenads were often given names connected with Attic drama or pre-dramatic events, even though their presence on the vases did not specify a ritual, a dramatic scene, or even a particular mythical episode. The satyrs named Marsyas on this vase definitely do not represent the satyr of legendary fame, for there are no attributes of the legend present, and Marsyas the satyr appears in vase-painting and mural-painting only in conjunction with Athena, Apollo, and Olympos.

Inscriptions indicate that bronze stamnoi existed, and this may account for the appearance of a few stamnoi painted entirely black, as if in imitation of metalware. The Attic stamnos was most popular in the Greek world from ca. 575 to ca. 420 B.C. and was heavily traded in Italy and Sicily, where most stamnoi have been excavated.

The Midas Painter belongs to the Group of Polygnotos. The work of Polygnotos the vase painter must be distinguished from that of Polygnotos, the famed mural-painter. However, in the mid-fifth century work of both mural painters and vase painters one notes the same idealization of the human face, the same refined perfection in the representation of drapery and furniture, and the same monumentality of stances. In this vase by the Midas Painter, the high quality of the Polygnotan free style can be seen in the nobility and grandeur of the figures, the idealized types with fine, even profiles, and the classic poses, which reveal the general influence of contemporary sculpture.

Only four stamnoi have been attributed to the Midas Painter, but in all his drawing-style is consistent: his figures have well-proportioned bodies and full, yet idealized faces with plump, rounded chins on the unbearded faces. Particularly characteristic of his style is the manner of depicting the eyes: many fine lines reveal a large pupil against the upper lid, drawn with two lines, and a delicately arched brow. The Midas Painter's other three stamnoi present similar subject matter (London E449, London E447, and Vatican, from Vulci: Beazley, *ARV²* 1035, nos. 1–3): on Side A, scenes like Eos driving her chariot over the sea and Silenos before Midas; on Side B, a maenad conversing with satyrs. The compositions of satyr and maenad on Side B are very consistent: typical are the upraised hands of the conversing satyrs, the restrained, calm poses of the period, the knobby hand with upturned thumbs and black tails of the satyrs. Hardly any anatomical details or lines can be seen within the drawn bodies: there is great simplicity of expression, as seen in the reserved u-shaped ankles. On Side A of this vase and London E447, maenads identically cock their heads over their shoulders. The drawing is general and defines broad areas but nevertheless is extremely beautiful.

Dimensions: H. 37.3 cm.

Description: Black glaze applied evenly throughout, reserving the figural and ornamental decoration and several junctions of the steps in the foot. On Side A, red once outlined the strings hanging from the young satyr's wineskin, the six strings of the lyre, and the flames of the maenad's torches. No red paint, if any was applied, appears on Side B.

Inscriptions: Red paint was used on Side A to inscribe ΔΙΟΝΥΣΟΣ over the god, ΜΑΡΣ[. . .] over the lyre-playing satyr, ΜΑΡΣΥΑΣ over the young satyr, and [. . .]ΛΙΚΕ over the maenad. (Baur has suggested Melike for the maenad, *Stoddard Catalogue,* 88; Beazley proposed Helike, *ARV²* 1035).

Condition: Very bad condition, broken into many pieces and restored with plaster and clay.

Surface worn; dilute glaze remains only in the maenads' and Dionysos' tresses.

Provenance: From the Collection of the Marchese Mattenci, Florence.

Bibliography: Beazley, VA 172; Baur, *Stoddard Catalogue* 88–9, no. 132 Beazley, *ARV²* 1035, no. 4; Barbara Philippaki, *The Attic Stamnos* (Oxford 1967) 133, pl. 55,2. On Dionysiac rituals and the stamnos: T.B.L. Webster, *Potter and Patron in Classical Athens* (Oxford 1968) 30–33; August Frickenhaus, *Lenäenvasen* (Berlin 1912). On the subject of Marsyas: Edoardo Galli, "Marsia Sileno," *Memorie della R. Accademia dei Lincei,* series 5, vol. 16 (1920) 4–54.

M. M. B.

61. Red-Figure Squat Lekythos

Attic. Follower of the Meidias Painter. Late fifth century B.C. *Stoddard Collection. Yale University Art Gallery 1913.152.*

Squat lekythoi became popular in the second half of the fifth century as perfume vases for women. In keeping with their function, most squat lekythoi are decorated with scenes of women and women's activities.

Aphrodite sits in a rocky landscape facing left but looking around; a rabbit appears in the laurel bushes to her right. Poseidon stands beyond the bushes flanked by Amymone, who is seated, and Amphitrite. The figures, are identified by partially

61

61

preserved inscriptions. Poseidon and Amymone also carry their attributes: Poseidon holds a trident and Amymone is seated next to a hydria. As is common is vase decoration of the late fifth century, the figures do not represent any particular mythological scene but instead are combined in an associative grouping inspired by the theme of "Poseidon as Lover." Amphitrite is, of course, Poseidon's wife; Amymone, one of the Danaids, was seduced by Poseidon; and Aphrodite seems to be present as a representation of sexual desire. The distinctly amorous overtones of the subject are emphasized by the presence of the rabbit, an animal traditionally associated with courtship.

This type of scene, with its romantic connotations and the somewhat miscellaneous grouping of figures, is typical of many vases by the Meidias painter and his school. Other details, such as the use of relief for the jewelry (once decorated with gold), the affected poses and gestures, the elaborate drapery which clings to the body, and the love of the laurel bush, all derive from the Meidian tradition. But although the Yale squat lekythos is close to the style of the Meidias Painter, the sharp, brittle quality of the line and the presence of a figure in white (Amymone) indicates the work of a follower. There is also a certain stiffness in the pose of Amphitrite rarely found on vases securely attributed to the Meidias Painter.

Dimensions: H. 20.3 cm. as restored.

Description: Type III squat lekythos, foot in three degrees, the lower part reserved. Below the scene a band of egg and dart. Palmettes with bird finials below the handle; a chain of smaller palmettes between reserved ridges at the shoulder. Tongues on the neck. Red: inscriptions; white: Amymone's drapery. Incision: lines describing rocky ground. Dilute glaze: Aphrodite's, Poseidon's, and Amphitrite's hair, folds on Amymone's white drapery. Relief: berries on laurel branches, Poseidon's wreath.

Inscriptions:

ΑΦ[. . . .] by Aphrodite;

[ΑΜ]ΦΙΤΡΤΗ   by Amphitrite;

ΠΟΣΕΙΔΩ[Ν] by Poseidon;

[ΑΜΥ]ΜΩΝΗ by Amymone

Condition: Badly damaged. The missing pieces have been restored and painted. The spout is added from an Italian squat lekythos.

Bibliography: Baur, *Stoddard Catalogue* 102–3, pl. 11 with earlier publications. On the Meidias group see: George Nicole, *Meidias et le style fleuri dans la Céramique Attique* (Geneva 1908); Pericle Ducati, "I vasi dipinti nello stile del ceramista Midia," *Memorie della R. Accademia dei Lincei,* Series 5, 14 (1900) 95–173; Walter Hahland, *Vasen um Meidias* (Berlin 1930); Giovanni Becatti; *Meidias, un manierista antico* (Florence 1947); Beazley, *ARV*² 1312–15.

C. B.

62. Red-Figure Bell Krater

Attic. Attributed to the Painter of Louvre G433. Ca.425–400 B.C. Stoddard Collection. Yale University Art Gallery 1913.129.

On side A, five figures cavort in a rocky landscape. The central figure moves to the right, looking back. He is beardless and wears a patterned chiton with a short fancy tunic worn over it, fastened by a plain belt. His long hair is loosely tied with a *tainia* and adorned with a wreath that is indicated by white dots. He wears high boots. In one hand he holds a flaming torch, in the other a somewhat problematic staff. This central figure is flanked by four satyrs, three dancing, one standing still. Two of these satyrs wear fawn skins, all wear wreaths, the one on the far right is clearly ivy. Three satyrs hold flaming torches, the fourth holds a thyrsos.

The identification of the central figure has been the cause of some discussion. Baur declared him to be Dionysos, which seems credible in view of the assembled company and his own youthful appearance. However, as Beazley points out ("Prometheus" 626–30), Dionysos only rarely holds a torch. The staff in this figure's other hand was called a sceptre by Baur, but while sceptres often have the sort of barberpole banding shown here, the cup-like head suggests something entirely different. In any case, it is equally rare for Dionysos to be shown holding a sceptre. Beazley suggests that this object may be a narthex (a giant stalk of fennel) with a cup-like top from which flames rise. The narthex serves as the shaft for the thyrsos and as such is often held by Dionysos. But perhaps more appropriately it was in such a stalk of giant fennel that Prometheus brought fire from Heaven. A figure holding a similar object with flames issuing forth from its top is identified by inscription as Prometheus on a calyx krater by the Painter of the Berlin Dinos in Oxford (Ashmolean Museum 1937.983, Beazley "Prometheus" 618

62, Side A

pl. 13); he too is surrounded by satyrs. Beazley suggests that in this case the scene may reflect a satyrplay connected with the Promethean trilogy of Aeschylus.

Three securely identified representations of the subject occur on red-figure vessels dating ca. 440–420 B.C. (identified by Beazley: Oxford, Ashmolean 1937.983, above; calyx krater, by an imitator of the Dinos Painter, Collection Feuardent, Paris; calyx krater, style of Polygnotos, 430's B.C., Bologna 288 bis). All show a bearded Prometheus. Moreover, there is no trace of flames issuing forth from the narthex. A certain identification of the scene must thus remain elusive.

On side B, in a standard scene, two draped youths stand with one arm outstretched on either side of a boy. The boy wears a himation which covers all but his head.

The Painter of Louvre G433 is linked to the Pronomos Painter, one of the major proponents of the late fifth century ornate/florid style. A bell krater in Berlin (inv. 2642, Beazley, ARV^2 1336, no. 2) was executed jointly by the two painters, side B (three youths) attributed to the Painter of Louvre G433 and side A (Dionysos with Eros, maenads and satyrs) attributed to the Pronomos Painter. The Painter of Louvre G433 shares an interest in theatrical subjects with the Pronomos

62, Side B, detail

side to the level of mid-thigh and the lower leg below the bent knee. The mid-section of the central figure is restored. The left figure is mostly complete except for restoration of the chin and neck.

Provenance: Nazzano.

Bibliography: Baur, *Stoddard Catalogue* 86, pl. 7; J.D. Beazley, *Etruscan Vase-painting* (Oxford 1947) 92, note 2; J.D. Beazley, "*Prometheus Fire-Lighter*," *AJA* 43 (1959) 626–30; Frank Brommer, *Satyrspiele* (Berlin 1959) 83, cat no. 190; Beazley, *ARV²* 1343, no. 3; Brommer, *Vasenlisten* 545, no. 8. On the subject, see further Adolf Greifenhagen, *Ein Satyrspiel des Aischylos? Winckelmannspro-gramm* 118 (Berlin 1963).

S. M. B.

Painter; the latter's name vase, a volute krater in Naples (inv. 3420, Beazley, *ARV²* 1336, no. 1) shows Dionysos and the cast of a satyr play on side A. Also shared with this artist, in whose workshop the Painter of Louvre G433 may well have trained, are the patterned garments and the arrangement of figures on different and often overlapping planes. These characteristics ultimately derive from the Dinos Painter, whose dependence on theatrical subjects is clearly demonstrated by the representation of Prometheus as Fire-lighter on the Oxford krater.

Dimensions: H. 36.8 cm.; diam. mouth 40.8 cm.

Description: Below the scene a band of quadruple meanders alternating with checkerboard squares. Below each handle an upright palmette; at the base of the handles an egg pattern. On the lip, laurel wreath. Red: rocks on side A. White: flames on the torches on side A as well as dots on the wreaths worn by the central figure and the two satyrs on the left; side B: fillets on all three figures.

Condition: Broken and repaired, with missing pieces restored and painted. Painted restoration along the break lines. Some losses, notably the face of the satyr holding the thyrsos and approximately one third of the cup-like top of the tall staff held by the central figure on side A. One handle partly restored; upper part of palmette under handles restored. Brown discoloration on many figures. Restoration to the figures on side A: mainly along the break lines, except most of the legs of the satyr on the extreme left are restored; side B: the back of the head of the figure on the right is restored, as well as his shoulder and right

WHITE-GROUND LEKYTHOI

Lekythoi and oinochoai were the most common burial offerings in the Classical period. The former occur in two forms, the squat red-figure lekythos and the tall cylindrical lekythos, usually white-ground. Both vessels were originally destined for domestic use; the white-ground lekythos evolved into a purely funerary object because the fragile quality of its decoration made it impractical for everyday use.

The earliest white-ground lekythoi are technically the same as black-figure, except that black glaze is applied over a white slip rather than the normal reserved red ground. An example by the Beldam Painter (cat. no. 37) is typical. The introduction of outline drawing was necessary for the white-ground lekythos to achieve its characteristic form. On early examples (ca. 475–450 B.C.) this outline drawing was executed in a brown dilute glaze like that used for some details in red-figure painting. This technique was used on other white-ground vessels, including kylikes, alabastra, and pyxides, until ca. 440 B.C.; beyond that date only white-ground lekythoi were produced. Artists of the mature and late lekythoi used a matte black or red for their drawing, a more fluid medium than the dilute glaze. A looser drawing style resulted.

Solid colors were often used to enhance the composition. At first red and an additional, snowy white were common, the former for garments and the latter for female flesh and other details. Additional colors were introduced by the Achilles Painter and his followers at mid-century. These included yellow, purple, blue, and green, a range of color denied to red-figure painters. These solid colors were not fired and were thus especially fugitive; often no trace of their presence is preserved and garments appear only in outline.

Many white-ground lekythoi were decorated by artists known to us from their red-figure work. The white-ground lekythoi by the Achilles Painter, for example, although unsigned, are clearly identifiable on the basis of similarities to his red-figure style. Even when unrelated to specific red-figure artists, the early white-ground lekythoi display much of the classical restraint and economy of line of their red-figure counterparts. Late white-ground lekythoi diverge in style from red-figure work of the later fifth century; the use of the matte black or red promotes a loose, fluid style not possible in the red-figure technique.

The scenes on white-ground lekythoi have greatly enhanced our knowledge of funerary practices in Classical Athens. Visits to the tomb by mourners bearing offerings are common subjects, as are domestic scenes of preparation for these visits. Less typical but equally enlightening are prothesis scenes showing the dead person laid out on a bier accompanied by mourners. Lekythoi appear as offerings on both sides of these scenes; depictions of burial mounds and grave stelai give a general idea of the appearance of the grave. Some emotion occurs among the mourners (tearing of hair or lying prostrate on the ground) but a restrained dignity is far more typical. The possible juxtaposition of the living and the dead in the tomb scenes remains an unsolved question. No differentiation of costume or other convention suggests a standard interpretation, and parallels among stone grave stelai are wanting.

The earlier of the two white-ground lekythoi exhibited here (cat. no. 63) shows a youth and a girl at a tomb. The youth ties a fillet around the stele, the girl brings offerings of an alabastron and a flower (?). The stele is shown atop the burial mound, a rather rare early representation of the tumulus that becomes quite frequent in later white-ground lekythoi (for another early example, but without the stele, see Walter Riezler, *Weissgrundige attische Lekythen* [Munich 1914] pl. 29, Athens 1960, ca. 470–460 B.C.; later examples include Ernst Buschor, "Attische Lekythen der Parthenonzeit," *Münchener Jahrbuch der bildenden Kunst,* new series, 2 [1925] fig. 12, ca. 425 B.C.;

J. D. Beazley, *Attic White Lekythoi* [London 1938] pl. IV, 1 [Bosanquet Painter, 440's B.C., Athens 1935]; Arthur Fairbanks, *Athenian White Lekythoi* [New York 1907] 206–8, class V, 22). The second, snowy white of the grave monument and the girl's flesh date this lekythos to the 460's. Beazley attributes it to the Painter of Athens 1826.

The matte red drawing of the second lekythos indicates that it is the later of the two. Again, a youth and a girl visit a tomb. Although somewhat generalized, the grave monument is close to standard fifth century Athenian types with palmette akroteria.

63. White-Ground Lekythos

Attic. Attributed to the Painter of Athens 1826. Ca. 460 B.C. Lent by Mr. and Mrs. Walter Bareiss; Bareiss no. 105.

Dimensions: H. 24.6 cm.
Description: Rightward meander between double black bands above the scene. Three palmettes and two flowers on a white-ground shoulder. Egg and dart at base of neck. Second white: grave mound, girl's flesh, and her alabastron. Youth's himation probably red.
Condition: Broken and repaired, with painted restorations.
Bibliography: Beazley, ARV² 1668, no. 5 bis; Beazley, *Paralipomena* 413.

64. White-Ground Lekythos

Attic. The Reed Painter. Ca. 440–425 B.C. Lent by Mr. and Mrs. Walter Bareiss; Bareiss no. 429.

Dimensions: H. 23.2 cm.
Description: Matte red drawing and hair. Lower part of girl's himation black. Probably a black wreath with streamers on front of the stele. Shoulder palmettes drawn in red and black.
Condition: Surface abraded, especially on back.
Bibliography: unpublished; attributed by Dietrich von Bothmer.

S. M. B.

63

64

LATER RED-FIGURE VASES

65. Red-Figure Pelike

Attic. Early Kerch Group. Workshop of the Hippolytus Painter. Ca. 375 B.C. Stoddard Collection. Yale University Art Gallery 1913.138.

Herakles in the Garden of the Hesperides appears on side A. The version of the last labor of Herakles represented here became popular at the end of the fifth century. In it, Herakles, having gone to the garden and obtained the help of the guardian nymphs, acquires the apples, the symbols of his immortality for the completion of his tasks. Herakles here sits on his lion skin in a quiet relaxed posture. The Hesperides surrounding him assume statueque poses. The apples, the goal of his mission, are being picked by one of the nymphs and an Eros who flies among the branches of the tree. The figures cover the large pictorial field, and the

laboring Hesperid to the left and the Hesperid and seated Pan at the right effectively frame the composition and echo the shape of the vase. All internal attention is focused on Herakles. Although the seated Hesperid is the actual center of the composition, her glance and the Eros who is perched on Herakles' knee direct the eye of the spectator to the heroic figure of Herakles. Even the evil effects of the snake, Ladon, are neutralized by his harmless, almost caressing, pose in the tree above Herakles' head.

This idyllic scene contrasts greatly with earlier representations of the labor. On archaic vases, a lively and often violent picture of the action is shown; the battle of the hero with the snake or the taking of the apples. In the fifth century, the moment depicted is usually Herakles' receiving the apples, a choice of scene which retains the sense of mission. Another version of the myth in which Herakles persuades Atlas to perform his task while the hero bears Atlas' burden, the weight of the world, is a concurrent theme in the fifth cen-

65, Side A

65, Side B

tury, as seen on the famous metope from the Temple of Zeus at Olympia. In the fourth century, although the other episodes of Herakles' struggle for immortality are rarely shown, the venture in the Garden of the Hesperides is more frequently depicted than ever before (see Frank Brommer, *JdI*, p. 116). Another vase with the scene in the Garden (British Museum E 227, *CVA* III Ic pl. 93,2) was also found in the Cyrenaica, which many ancients thought to be the home of the Hesperides.

On side B a maenad in full frontal view runs to the left, while looking back over her shoulder. Her right arm is raised; her left is extended and holds a thyrsos. Her sleeveless chiton is fastened on the shoulders and banded with a thick line at the hem and the bottom of the *apoptygma*. Folds are only sketchily indicated with quick thin lines. Behind her a nude satyr follows in rapid pursuit. He is bearded and snub-nosed and the pose of his limbs echoes that of the maenad's. An Eros hovers in front of the maenad, flying in the direction of her escape route, but looking back at the scene behind him. He holds a large tympanum in his left hand. The quick succession of the three figures, the similarity of poses, and even the maenad's chiton overlapping the satyr's leg give a blurred impression of speed which the cursory execution of drapery and detail enhance.

The last phase of Attic red-figure vase painting is known as the Kerch style, named after the city in South Russia where three hundred vases, more than half of the total known, were discovered. They were exported widely, not only to the Crimea, but also within Greece and to the southern shores of the Mediterranean. The style is strongly plastic in conception, recalling the sculptures of Praxiteles and Skopas. The predeliction for three-quarter poses and the finely delineated anatomy and drapery infuse a three-dimensionality into the figures. Bodies, covered or nude, have an independent corporeality which gives life to the often repeated poses.

Dimensions: H. 39.1 cm.

Description: Above the figures on side A is a broad band of egg-and-dot pattern below a narrow band of the same pattern. On side B, another broad band of the same pattern runs above the figures. Circling the vase below the figures is an egg-and-dot band. Below and at the base of each handle are palmettes.

Condition: Handles broken and repaired; pieces missing at base of each. Neck and mouth restored incorrectly; lip should overhang and be offset. Un-

even glaze; surface worn and unevenly preserved. Some preliminary drawing in inner markings of anatomy and drapery. Added white: flesh of Erotes and serpent (now largely missing); also perhaps for added clay of apples and jewelry (also missing).

Provenance: Dernah in the Cyrenaica.

Bibliography: Baur, *Stoddard Catalogue* 92–94, no. 138, fig. 26; Karl Schefold, *Untersuchungen zu den kertscher Vasen* (Berlin and Leipzig 1934) no. 543, pp. 57, 66, 90, 145; Frank Brommer, "Herakles und die Hesperiden auf Vasenbildern," *JdI* 57 (1942) 118, IIb8; Henri Metzger, *Les représentations dans la céramique attique du IVe siècle* (Paris 1951) 203, no. 20; Brommer, *Vasenlisten* 41, no. 16; Rudolf Horn, *Stehende weibliche Gewandstatuen in der hellenistischen Plastik (Ergänzungsheft der Mitteilungen des deutschen archäologischen Instituts, Römische Abteilung, 2* [Munich 1931]) 90; Paul Jacobsthal, *Ornamente griechischer Vasen* (Berlin 1927) 202, no. 369.

M. E. C. S.

66. Red-Figure Bell Krater

South Italian, Early Lucanian. Attributed to the Dolon Painter. Late fifth century B.C. *Stoddard Collection. Yale University Art Gallery 1913. 322.*

On side A a nude young Dionysos with a garment thrown over his left shoulder and arm holds a thyrsos and wears a red wreath in his hair. His right hand extends in a graceful gesture towards

66, Side B, detail

66, Side A

the left hand of a maiden offering him a kylix. The woman, most probably a maenad, is draped in a short chiton. She wears a red necklace, snake bracelets, earrings, and an elaborate cap or *sakkos*. She carries a pail in her right hand, and behind her stands a silen who leans on his staff. His folded arms wrap the himation closer to him and characterize his stance as animated observer. His head is typically large and expressive, and in his mass of black hair with straggling ends, he wears a red fillet. His goat ears, arched eyebrows, beard tucked close to his chest, and his bulging eyes, create an unmistakably comic mask. This burlesque treatment of the silen contrasts with the graceful gestures, stance, and facial treatment of the other two figures. There is then a somewhat subtle interplay that borders on the dramatic. This is especially well executed by the designer of this vase, the Dolon Painter, who is a member of the so-called Proto-Lucanian group. Several bell kraters by the Dolon Painter similar to the Yale krater in shape, pattern, and composition exhibit the standard three-figure group of Dionysos, maenad, and silen so popular in this period of the mythical burlesque and flourishing theater in Southern Italy. Three in particular reflect the same stylistic treatment and expressive gestures: San Simeon Hearst Estate 5608 (Noël Moon, "Some Early South Italian Vase Painters," *Papers of the British School at Rome* II [1929] pl. 14.2); Bari 6267 (Trendall, *LCS* pl. 50, no. 4); once Paris Market, ex Hope 214 (E.M.W. Tillyard, *The Hope Vases* [Cambridge 1923] pl. 30,6).

On side B stand three draped young men or

67, Side A

ephebi. This is the stock theme on the reverses of the Dolon Painter's vases. The Yale group, like the others, is done in a sketchy and untidy fashion when compared to the finer execution of the obverse. These characters have large curly heads, with straggling hair and large droopy mouths. Because of the obvious stylistic differences between the obverse and reverse of many of the Dolon Painter's vases, it seems logical to conclude that the reverses were painted by various members of the workshop, rather than by the master himself.

Dimensions: H. 30.42 cm.; D. 30.36 cm.

Description: Light brown clay and light brown varnish. Typical inverted bell with loop handles placed high on the body and curving upwards. At lip, a running border of laurel-wreath pattern;

below each group a band of stopped meander and saltire crosses in panels. At the juncture of the handles is a short panel of black tongues.

Condition: Intact, surface well preserved.

Provenance: Said to be from Bari.

Bibliography: Baur: *Stoddard Catalogue* no. 322, pl. 16, fig. 83; A.D. Trendall, *Early South Italian Vase-Painting* (Mainz 1974) 44s, no. 503. See text p. 10s for general discussion of Dolon Painter.

C. K.

67. Red-Figure Bell Krater

Lucanian. Attributed to the Choephori Painter. 360–330 B.C. Stoddard Collection. Yale University Art Gallery 1913.323.

67, Side B

Greek on horseback wearing a chlamys, petasos and sandals wields a lance at an Amazon. She is dressed in a fashion typical of Attic representations in a short chiton with an oriental cap but wears boots where her Attic sisters are normally barefoot. She is armed with an axe and a crescent shaped shield (*pelta*), and a quiver hangs from her left shoulder. The duel between a Greek on horseback and an Amazon is known from three classic period red-figure examples (Dietrich von Bothmer, *Amazons in Greek Art* [Oxford 1957] 193–4) and seems to be a red-figure distillation of larger black-figure Amazonomachies with mounted Greeks.

On side B, in a standard scene, a youth talks to a woman and a silen.

The mature fourth century Lucanian style follows directly from that of the Dolon and Creusa Painters, active ca. 400–360 B.C. Of the second generation Lucanian painters, the Choephori Painter and the Primato Painter are the best and most individual. The Choephori Painter is named for a group of six vases showing Orestes, Electra and others at the tomb of Agamemnon, a scene generally associated with the *Choephori* of Aeschylus (J.H. Huddilston, *Greek Tragedy in the Light of Vase Paintings* [London 1898] 43–55; A.D. Trendall, "Choephori Painter," 116–117, 120–122; *LCS* 118 ff). Characteristic of the Choephori Painter's style are the three-quarter face of the Greek, with a square jaw framed by straggly locks, the three-quarter body view of the silen, with the head in profile and the legs crossed, and the embattled border on the woman's chiton. His border patterns and palmettes are equally consistent. His style is heavily indebted to the Dolon-Creusa Group, and Trendall suggests that he must have studied in their workshop. A bell krater in Madrid of which one side was painted by the Creusa Painter and the other by the Choephori Painter strengthens this suggestion (inv. 11091, Trendall, *LCS* 119).

Dimensions: H. 40.5 cm.

Description: Below the design, a band of meanders in groups of four alternating with squares divided into four compartments with dots. Tongue pattern at the base of the handles. Under the handles palmettes, ending in roughly serrated edges. Laurel wreath encircles the mouth. A branch in the field of the Amazon duel, a spotted fillet hanging between the youth and the woman on side B.

Condition: Broken and repaired, missing pieces restored and painted.

Bibliography: Baur, *Stoddard Catalogue* 189, fig. 84, pl. 16–17; H. Speier, "Zweifiguren-Gruppen in fünften und vierten Jahrhundert vor Christus," *RömMitt* 47 (1932) 75, pl. 18,4; A.D. Trendall, "The Choephori Painter," *Studies Presented to David Moore Robinson* II (St. Louis 1953) 118–119, 122–123; Trendall, *LCS* 121, cat. 609, pl. 61, 1–2.

S. M. B.

68. Red-Figure Pelike

South Italian, Apulian. Ca. 350 B.C. Stoddard Collection. Yale University Art Gallery 1913. 258.

On side A, in the center of the composition, is a plump male with long curls. He wears a decorated fillet and is draped from the waist down. He is seated with his left elbow resting on two embroidered cushions. In his left hand he holds a phiale from which his right hand has taken some white objects. A dappled fawn grazes below him. In front of the man stands a woman in profile who bends forward, offering the man the wreath in her extended right hand. Her left arm, holding a bunch of grapes, rests on her raised left knee. An open chest is at a higher level behind her. Behind the man stands another woman who holds a mirror in her outstretched right hand and a decorated plate by her left side. Her chiton is elaborately

banded, and an untied fillet curves gracefully above her head. Both women wear colored jewelry and accessories and yellow shoes. Seated on a himation above the man is an Eros whose elaborately colored wings are extended to either side of him. In his left hand, he holds a wand, in his right, a wreath. A laurel branch and flowers rise from the lowest ground line.

On side B a nude man holds a phiale in his right hand which is decorated with white dots and seems to hold similar white objects. He is seated on his himation and wears a wreath of thick white rays. On either side of him stands a woman, one almost a true mirror image of the other. Each holds a mirror in the hand extended to the youth and a wreath with black dots in the hand by her side. Above each is a fillet, outlined in white with long streamers. An Eros holding a double wreath in both hands flies to the left above the head of the youth.

Apulian vase painting which started during the last quarter of the fifth century and continued throughout the fourth century was centered primarily in Taranto. It is interesting to note that once established, it quickly gained control of the local market, virtually excluding further Attic and Lucanian imports. The two branches, the Plain Style and the Ornate Style, are both descended from the Sisyphus Painter. Painters of the Plain Style based their work on his more simply decorated vases of normal size, with little or no added color. Painters of the Ornate Style used more monumental conceptions, often mythological in content, with profuse added color.

This vase stands close to the Lycurgus Painter, a prominent painter of the Ornate Style, who dates to the second quarter of the fourth century. Our painter shares with him the use of statuesque poses, a variety of ground lines to suggest depth, floral motifs, gay coloring, and the delicate rendering of drapery. The similarities, however, raise problems, for the repertory of motifs in South Italy was limited and widely employed, sometimes with apparent disregard for the original iconographical significance. For example, the fawn appears on two works of the Lycurgus Painter with Dionysiac representations (Andrew Oliver, Jr., "Lycurgus Painter," figs. 3 & 4) and on another vase showing the Judgment of Paris (A.D. Trendall, *Vasi antichi dipinti del Vaticani* II [Vatican City 1953–5] pl. 50). Our scene has no definite relation to either context. Similarly, the open chest, mirrors, grapes, fillets, wreaths, and phialai appear in funereal, nuptial, and Dionysiac scenes (e.g., A. D. Trendall, *ibid.*, pls. 49 and 50 and Trieste, *CVA* 43, IVd, pls. 11 and 12). While the use of motifs may not have been as indiscriminate as it appears, the repetition of such items tends to obscure their meaning. Our painter, while related to the Lycurgus Painter, is not as masterful. His faces are all rendered in profile, although most figures are in three-quarter view. Ground lines or even the supports of seated figures are not indicated. The various levels are meaningless without interaction between them. Side B, a simpler, stiffer version of the scene on Side A, reveals his reliance on stock figures with little concern for integrating the composition.

Dimensions: H. 42.5 cm.

Description: The body of the pelike is bulbous, but the proportionately wide and short neck balances the mass below it well. Its torus mouth is a shape which competes with the more common echinus form. The characteristic groove below the rim and the bottom and edge of the foot are reserved, a common feature of Apulian pelikai. On the neck are (A) alternating palmettes and lotus above an egg-and-dot band with yellow pendants below it; (B) a spray of laurel to the left between horizontal lines. On the handles, which are segmental in section, are branches of laurel and maltese crosses. Below them are palmettes. Below the figural group is a band of stopped meander with occasional rectangles filled with saltire crosses or with checkers.

Condition: Intact. Surface wear with damage to glaze. Some traces of preliminary drawing. Considerable amount of added yellow and white paint on accessories and decoration.

Bibliography: Baur, *Stoddard Catalogue* 157–

68, Side A

68, Side B

158, no. 258, fig. 64. For Apulian: Arturo Stenico, "Vasi, Apuli," *Enciclopedia dell'Arte Antica* I, pp. 502–509 with bibliography. More recently, Alexander Cambitoglou and A. D. Trendall, *Apulian Red-Figured Vase-Painters of the Plain Style* (Archaeological Institute of America 1961); A.D. Trendall, *Early South Italian Vase Painting* (Mainz 1974). For the Lycurgus Painter: Margo Schmidt, *Der Dariosmaler und sein Umkreis* (Munich 1960) 12–17; Andrew Oliver, Jr., "The Lycurgus Painter; An Apulian Artist of the Fourth Century B.C.," *Metropolitan Museum of Art Bulletin* 21 (1962) 25–30.

M. E. C. S.

GNATHIAN WARE

Gnathian Ware, a South Italian product, represents the triumph of the ornate. The principal decoration is applied color (red, white, and yellow) on a dark ground; some incision occurs as well, but only as a secondary technique. The style and technique probably derived from the prolific ornament of the Apulian Ornate Style of the fourth century B.C. White and yellow were commonly used to embellish figures and to add laurel wreaths and border motifs. In the mature Gnathian style these subsidiary elements became the primary decoration, often to the exclusion of figures. Vines, ivy, grapes and grape vines, wreaths, and laurel bands dominate. Decoration covers most of the vessel.

The shapes of Gnathian Ware are in the red-figure tradition and show many specific links with South Italian red-figure pottery. Kraters, pelikai, oinochoai of several types, squat lekythoi, and skyphoi are particularly close to their Apulian ancestors. Other shapes were modified to an extent. The Apulian shapes used show that the Gnathian style must have developed by the mid-fourth century; production continued for about a century, slightly longer in outlying areas. Vessels develop from their solid Apulian prototypes towards more elegant shapes, with narrow necks and feet, depressed globular bodies, and exaggerated curvature of the profile.

Early Gnathian Ware, especially the work of the Konnakis Painter and his circle (see T.B.L. Webster, "Towards a Classification of Apulian Gnathian," *Bulletin of the Institute of Classical Studies of the University of London* 15 [1968] 1–33 for a breakdown into painters and workshops), is closest to Apulian in subject matter. Theatrical subjects are common, showing full scenes in the earliest works, single figures or masks in later pieces.

The style was widespread in Italy. Major sites for Gnathian Ware finds have been Tarentum, Lecce, and Gnathia; but examples have been found throughout Greek Italy and Sicily, Etruria, Latium,

69, 72

France, and Spain. Some local variants were produced in Campania and Sicily. Early connections with Apulia suggest invention there.

69. Skyphos

Apulian. Gnathian Ware. 360–300 B.C. Stoddard Collection. Yale University Art Gallery 1913. 285.

Dimensions: H. 16.6 cm.; D. with handles 22 cm.

Description: Grapes and grape leaves suspended from a red band; leaves and white tendrils grow from the same red band. Row of yellow dots in groups of three above this, then a row of single yellow dots, incised lines, false white spiral, more incised lines, alternating red and yellow short horizontal bands, and egg and dart with dots between incised lines. Below the grape vine, rosettes. On side B an ivy spray of two incised lines and white leaves.

Condition: Lip chipped. White somewhat worn.

Bibliography: Baur, *Stoddard Catalogue* 173, fig. 73. For the hand, cf. Naples Harp Group (T.B.L. Webster, "Apulian Gnathian," 13).

70. Squat Lekthos

Apulian. Gnathian Ware. Ca. 330–320 B.C. Stoddard Collection. Yale University Art Gallery 1913.293.

Dimensions: max. pres. H. 14.5 cm.

Description: Foot in three degrees, black; reserved band above it. Painted and incised egg and dart with dots borders the main panel. Female head (white with yellow details) facing left between tendrils (white and yellow); in the center below the head a flower, probably a papyrus. Shoulder: 1 row of yellow dots below painted and incised egg and dart with dots (white) with incised bands. White vertical ribs at the base of the neck.

Condition: Upper neck and mouth missing. Foot broken and repaired, one piece missing.

Provenance: From Lecce.

Bibliography: Baur, *Stoddard Catalogue* 176. For the hand, cf. the Boston Group (T.B.L. Webster, "Apulian Gnathian," 22) or the Stockport group (T.B.L. Webster, "Masks on Gnathia Vases," *JHS* 71 [1951] 227 with additions in T.B.L. Webster, "Apulian Gnathian"), both from around 330–320 B.C.

71. Miniature Lebes Gamikos

Apulian. Gnathian Ware. Ca. 320–300 B.C. Stoddard Collection. Yale University Art Gallery 1913.272.

Dimensions: H. 10.8 cm. without handles.

Description: Foot in three degrees, reserved band above it. Egg and dart with dots (white) between incised lines below a swan facing left be-

71, 70

tween tendrils, (white and yellow). Shoulder: 2 projections painted white. Between them a row of dots in groups of three and a row of single dots placed below egg and dart with dots between incised lines. Side B: 2 vertical laurel sprays hang from a band of yellow dots below a band of egg and dart with dots within incised lines. A rosette between the sprays.

Condition: Minor surface losses on side A near the left handle.

Bibliography: Baur, *Stoddard Catalogue* 167–8. Similar in style to the Boston and Stockport Groups and the squat lekythos Yale 1913.293 (cat. no. 70; see previous entry for bibliography).

72. Squat Lekythos

Apulian. Gnathian Ware. Ca. 320–300 B.C. Stoddard Collection. Yale University Art Gallery 1913.282.

Dimensions: H. 21.7 cm.

Description: On the foot a band of white waves between incised lines. Concave sides partly encircled by a white laurel wreath with a red and white rosette in the center. Shoulder ledge: egg and dart with dots (white) and incised lines. Shoulder: seated woman between tendrils, with feet outstretched to left, body turned to right as she reaches for a swan walking left. She holds 2 sticks (torches?) in her other hand. White dress with red sleeves with yellow dots; red border at hem, red fillet. At the base of the neck a row of dots; vertical white ribs around base of the neck. Two faces in relief at base of handle where it joins neck.

Condition: Foot chipped and repaired, 1 piece from shoulder ledge repaired. Some paint loss, especially on waves and tendrils.

Provenance: From Lecce.

Bibliography: Baur, *Stoddard Catalogue* 171–2.

S. M. B.

MEGARIAN BOWLS

With the decline of red-figure vase painting at the end of the fourth century B.C., black glazed and molded relief wares gained in popularity. Megarian bowls, mainly of the third through second century B.C., were among the earliest of the molded wares to see commercial success. Examples of the basically hemispherical bowls have been found throughout the Hellenistic world. A broad range of fabrics suggests that the bowls were made in many Greek cities. Slight variations in shape appear to be localized: Attic bowls are deep with a lip that curves out; bowls from the eastern Aegean, especially a group from Delos, are shallower with a turned-in lip.

The technique for producing Megarian bowls was the same as that used in manufacturing terra sigillata ware in the Roman period. The potter first made a terra cotta mold. When this had dried to the leather hard stage, the decorative zones were marked off by incision, and clay stamps were used to impress the human figures, vegetable, floral or other motifs that provided the primary decoration. A medallion, usually, a rosette or a mask, was stamped into the bottom of the bowl. Occasionally the potter would stamp his own signature into the mold (cat. no. 73). That the incision was done before the stamping is shown by cat.no. 75, where the head of Herakles protrudes over the incised line. The bowl itself was made by pressing clay into this mold, then turning the two together on a wheel to form the bowl's interior and rim. As the bowl dried it shrank away from the mold, permitting its removal. It was then glazed and fired in the same manner as plain black glazed ware. The best quality metallic black glaze occurs on the early examples; later thinly glazed examples are fired mottled or red (Homer A. Thompson, "Two Centuries of Hellenistic Pottery," *Hesperia* III [1934] 452).

Few of the bowls have any sort of continuous narrative or even consistent subject matter, although an early group with Homeric scenes, probably made in Boeotia, has been isolated (Ulrich Hausmann, *Hellenistische Reliefbecher aus attischen und böotischen Werkstatten* [Stuttgart 1959]). Far more typical are figural bowls with numerous unrelated figures (cat. nos. 74 and 75), floral or vegetable motifs, or the long petals that resemble gadroons or fluting (cat. no. 73). The technique permitted an infinite variety of molds, depending on the number of stamps available to the potter as well as his own creativity in combining them. Few duplicate bowls have been found, suggesting that the potter was in fact interested in achieving this variety.

There is general agreement that Megarian bowls first appeared during the third century B.C. (but for a date at the end of the fourth century, see Fernand Courby, *Les vases grecs à relief* [Paris 1922] 333 and 360 ff and Willy Schwabacher, "Hellenistische Reliefkeramik im Kerameikos," *AJA* 45 [1941] 225). This conclusion is confirmed for Attica at least by the fact that at the Athenian Agora no Megarian bowls were found in conjunction with Red Figure pottery (Thompson, "Hellenistic Pottery," 457); a date after the end of the fourth century must thus be presumed. Thompson has developed an internal chronology for the bowls from the Agora finds. He considers the purely vegetable and floral bowls among the earliest, followed rapidly by the bowls with varied figural decoration, which were the most popular type in Athens from the mid-third to the second quarter of the second century B.C. The long petalled variety succeeded the figural bowls and was the favored type in the later second century.

Alexandria is most frequently mentioned as a possible site for the origin of Megarian bowls. Although certain motifs, particularly the lotus petal, seem to derive from characteristic motifs in Egyptian silver and faience bowls of the fourth and third centuries B.C. (Klaus Parlasca, "Das Verhältnis der megarischen Becher zum alexandrinischen Kunsthandwerk," *JdI* 70 [1955] 129–54), archaeological evidence confirming this suggested origin is lacking. The derivation of Megarian bowls from metal prototypes has likewise not been proven, but the relationship has been generally accepted on the basis of a number of similar early Hellenistic works in metal cited by Parlasca and others.

73. Megarian Bowl

Attic. Ca. 150–100 B.C. Stoddard Collection. Yale University Art Gallery 1913.199.

The same inscription on the same type of long petalled bowl occurs on an example from Anthedon now in Berlin (Robert Zahn, "Hellenistische Reliefgefässe aus Südrussland," *JdI* 23 [1908] 74, n. 31). Thompson ("Hellenistic Pottery," 458) believes this class originated in Athens, where molds

73

for them have been found in the Agora and the Pnyx. The long petal motif is known from bronze vessels and occurs later in Roman mold blown glass vessels.

Dimension: H. 8 cm., diam. 13.3 cm.

Description: Bottom indented, with rosette within a base ring. Long petals radiate from this ring. Buff fabric, mostly fired red.

Inscription: Molded, inside one petal: ΠΟΛΕΜΩΝΟΣ

Condition: Rim cracked and chipped.

Provenance: Acquired in Salonika.

Bibliography: Baur, *Stoddard Catalogue* 127–8 fig. 46; Thompson, "Hellenistic Pottery" 451–2, n. 3; Paul V.C. Baur, "Megarian Bowls in the Rebecca Darlington Stoddard Collection of Greek and Italian Vases in Yale University," *AJA* 45 (1941) 236–7, fig. 6.

74. Megarian Bowl

Attic. Ca. 250–150 B.C. Stoddard Collection. Yale University Art Gallery 1913.196.

There are three main groups in the frieze. In the first Dionysos is suported by a satyr and embraced by a maenad. They are accompanied by a Nike flying to the right and a dancing Eros in frontal view. The group is common on Megarian bowls and may reflect a Hellenistic sculptural group (Baur, "Megarian Bowls" 233–4 and Schwabacher, "Hellenistische Reliefkeramik" 187–8). The second group consists of a beardless man seated on a cliff holding a small, struggling, nude girl on his knees. Again the main figures are accompanied by a flying Nike and dancing Eros, with the addition here of dolphins swimming under-

74

75

neath. This group occurs on other Megarian bowls, mainly of Attic manufacture (Baur, "Megarian Bowls" 233–4). The third group appears to be a composite, consisting of Apollo and Artemis or Leto, and a woman crowning him. The last figure actually belongs to a different stamp group of two women and a trophy (see cat. no. 75). Baur's suggested Antiochene source for this bowl is rejected by Waagé.

Dimensions: H. 8.7 cm., diam. 12.5 cm.

Description: On the bottom a mask within three rings; two rows of palmettes outside the rings. Bands below the lip of scroll and ivy, volutes, and egg and dart.

Condition: Intact.

Provenance: Acquired in Salonika.

Bibliography: Baur, *Stoddard Catalogue* 125–6, fig. 46; Paul Baur, "Megarian Bowls" 223–4, pl. 13, fig. 2; Willy Schwabacher, "Hellenistische Reliefkermik" 187, 191, 194; Klaus Parlasca, "Alexandrinischen Kunsthandwerk" 152; F. O. Waagé, *Antioch on the Orontes* IV, pt. 1 (Princeton 1952) 30, n. 10.

75. Megarian Bowl

Boeotian. Ca. 250–150 B.C. Stoddard Collection. Yale University Art Gallery 1937.197.

Dimensions: H. 7.5 cm., diam. 12 cm.

Description: On the bottom a rosette of heart-shaped petals, within two rings from which radiate lotus petals and palmettes. Below the lip bands of egg and dart, and double spirals with palmettes. Main frieze: a) Dionysos riding a panther, attacking a fallen warrior with a thyrsos; b) helmeted warrior with a dagger or thunderbolt, in the latter case the figure would be Zeus; c) seated figure with shield; d) Athena attacking a bearded giant; e) two women offering a libation to a trophy consisting of a helmet, cuirass, and shield on a pile of stones; f) Herakles and the Nemean Lion.

Condition: Broken and repaired, small fragments missing. Glaze somewhat worn.

Provenance: Acquired in Salonika.

Bibliography: Baur, *Stoddard Catalogue* 126–7, fig. 46; Paul Baur, "Megarian Bowls" 229–32, pl. XI, fig. 1; Willy Schwabacher, "Hellenistiche Reliefkeramik" 192; Klaus Parlasca, "Alexandrinischen Kunsthandwerk" 152; Ulrich Hausmann, *Hellenistiche Reliefbecher* 27, 95.

S. M. B.